Solubility and pH Calculations

The Mathematics of the Simplest Ionic Equilibria

This book is in the

ADDISON-WESLEY SERIES
IN THE PRINCIPLES OF CHEMISTRY

————————————

Francis T. Bonner
Consulting Editor

Solubility and pH Calculations

The Mathematics of the Simplest Ionic Equilibria

by

JAMES NEWTON BUTLER

Head, Physical Chemistry Department
Tyco Laboratories, Waltham Mass.

Formerly Department of Chemistry
University of British Columbia
Vancouver, B.C.

ADDISON-WESLEY PUBLISHING COMPANY

Reading, Massachusetts · Menlo Park, California
London · Amsterdam · Don Mills, Ontario · Sydney

Second printing, April 1973

ISBN 0–201–00733–9
  OPQRSTU–AL–89876543

Preface

All students of elementary chemistry sooner or later encounter calculations relating to ionic equilibrium in solution. For many this is a confusing and frustrating experience. These problems usually involve some algebraic manipulation in addition to arithmetic, and many students have never previously encountered chemistry problems in which algebra was important. Students whose background in algebra is weak very often are unable to comprehend the mathematical steps involved in the solution of even the simplest ionic equilibrium problems, and feel as a result that they are unable to understand the chemistry behind the problem.

Many excellent textbooks have been written which try to explain the nature of equilibrium in a qualitative fashion. This little book is intended to approach the problem from the other direction, and is concerned with the mathematical aspects of simple ionic equilibrium calculations. The illustrative examples are worked out in great detail, considerable space is devoted to the use of graphical representations, and emphasis is placed on a rigorous approach to the solution of problems.

The approach used is the same as in my book *Ionic Equilibrium*, and many of the same examples and problems are included. For more details on any of the topics discussed, the reader is referred to the more extensive work.

The student who uses this book is assumed to be familiar with molar concentrations, elementary stoichiometry, and the general concept of equilibrium. No attempt has been made to discuss the nature of equilibrium or to derive the equilibrium laws.

A number of people have read this manuscript. J. A. R. Coope of the University of British Columbia and F. H. Firsching of the University of Georgia were particularly helpful with their extensive detailed suggestions for improving the treatment. For their comments I also wish to thank F. T. Bonner, S. Bruckenstein, W. A. Bryce, L. G. Harrison, K. B. Harvey, R. M. Hochstrasser, L. Nash, E. A. Ogryzlo, W. P. Schaefer, R. F. Snider, and F. D. Tabbutt.

The mountain-climbing allegory which introduces the chapters was inspired by a climb of Okie's Thorn on the East Ridge of the Grand Teton, Wyoming, in 1954.

The content of this book has been restricted to a very narrow range of subject matter, but I hope that it will help those students who find ionic equilibrium problems mysterious to clear up some of the mystery.

Waltham, Mass.   J. N. B.
November, 1963

Contents

Prologue

"There it is!" exclaimed my friend, who knew the mountain range like the back of his own hand. *"Some have called it 'Mustagh Tower' because it looks so inaccessible."* Before us rose a mighty tower of granite separated from the main ridge by a cleft of softer rock. It appeared from where we stood to be nearly smooth and overhanging on all sides.

"Some chap a few years back claimed he did it from the back side, up that rotten gully where all the rock falls keep coming down."

"If he made it," I said, *"he was damned lucky."*

My friend shaded his eyes from the sun and pointed. *"See that crack over there? It looks a little more difficult than the rotten gully, but if we can make it go, it will be a truly elegant climb. In any case, it will be good for an afternoon's amusement."*

Mathematical Background | 1

"When you start on such a climb as this," he said, opening his pack, "you have to make sure you have all your ironmongery in just the right order." He clipped pitons and karabiners to his waist loop in some mysteriously predetermined order, coiled the rope with loving patience, and finally closed his pack again. Hoisting it to his back, with the rope over his arm, he started along the broken rock ridge to the base of the pinnacle. I followed with a rather uneasy feeling in the pit of my stomach.

In this little book we shall be concerned with the problem of calculating the equilibrium concentrations in an aqueous solution from known equilibrium constants. For many elementary students, this is the most difficult mathematics they have encountered in their study of chemistry, and perhaps the most difficult they have encountered outside of courses in pure mathematics. The purpose of this book is to clear up some of the mystery surrounding equilibrium problems by very carefully stating the mathematical equations involved and the methods used to solve them.

Solving an equilibrium problem. Before we can begin to solve any equilibrium problems, however, we must be sure that we understand what we are going to do. Solving an equilibrium problem consists of a number of steps; some chemical, some mathematical:

1. *What species are present?* The nature of all the species present in the solution must be established. This involves very complicated experimental and theoretical procedures, and for many chemical systems the nature of the species present in aqueous solution is as yet not completely known. In the problems we do, we shall give this information to the extent that it is known at present.

2. *What are the equilibrium constants?* The equilibrium constants relating the concentrations of the various species must be found. These are often determined in the same investigation in which the nature of the species in solution is established. A brief table of constants, which are used in the

1

examples and problems in this book, is given in the appendix. For precise calculations, the tabulated constant must be corrected for the electrostatic and chemical forces between ions in a solution of finite concentration. We shall consider this point more thoroughly in Section 2–4.

3. *What other relations are needed?* Enough other relations between the unknown concentrations must be found so that there are as many equations as unknowns. One way of doing this is to consider the stoichiometry of the reactions forming the equilibrium species, and this "method of the principal reaction" is usually used in elementary textbooks. A more fruitful, but perhaps more complicated way is to use mass and charge balances. We shall employ this latter method; as individual systems are discussed in Chapters 2, 3, and 4, we shall introduce the appropriate mass and charge balances.

4. *Solve the equations.* This system of n simultaneous equations in n unknowns must be solved for all the unknown concentrations. This part of the problem is strictly mathematical, but it can be made much easier if it is possible to make approximations on the basis of our chemical knowledge. As many approximations are made as seem reasonable, and the approximate equations are solved.

5. *Check the answers.* The approximate answers are checked by substitution in the original exact equations. If these equations are not satisfied to within the desired accuracy, new approximations are made, and the new approximate equations are solved. If the exact equations are still not satisfied, some of the approximations must be discarded. Eventually a set of answers is obtained which satisfies the original exact equations to within the desired accuracy.

6. *Pick the answer you need.* One of these answers, usually the concentration of hydrogen ions or a solubility, is the answer needed for application to the chemical problem.

How to approach a complicated problem. Since the problems that we shall encounter here are often quite a bit more complicated than you are used to, it is very important that you keep a clear head and know what you are doing when you solve them. In his book, *How to Solve It*, G. Polya sets out four equally important steps in problem solving:

1. *You have to understand the problem.* What are the unknowns? What are the knowns? What condition relates them?

2. *Make a plan of solution.* Do you know a related problem? Look at the unknown. Do you know a problem with the same unknown? Is it related to the problem at hand? Go back to definitions. Can you solve part of the problem? Can you solve the problem with slightly different conditions? Could you change the data or unknown so that they are more closely related?

3. *Carry out the plan of solution, checking each step as you go.* Is each step reasonable? Can you prove that each step is correct?

4. *Examine the solution.* Is the result reasonable? If the problem is symmetrical with respect to one of the unknowns, is the solution also symmetrical with respect to that unknown? Do the numerical answers fall within the limits imposed by the statement of the problem? Does a complicated answer reduce to a simpler, known answer under special conditions? For what other problems could you use this method or this result?

Keeping these rules in mind will make solution of the problems in this book much easier and much more instructive.

1–1 SIMULTANEOUS EQUATIONS

It is a rare problem in equilibrium that does not involve at least three unknowns, and many problems encountered in practice may involve as many as fifteen or twenty unknowns. The equations relating the unknowns are usually not linear, and hence the methods of determinants or adding and subtracting equations, which are taught in most algebra courses, cannot be applied. The only general method which is left for dealing with *nonlinear* simultaneous equations is the method of *substitution*.

The exact solution of a system of simultaneous equations is straightforward and need not be confusing if it is approached systematically.

Proceed in the following manner:

1. *Pick the unknown which occurs in the least number of equations.* Call it z_1.*

2. *Find all the equations which contain z_1.* If only one equation contains this unknown, set the equation aside until the end and work with the remaining $n - 1$ equations, beginning at step 1.

3. *Solve one equation for z_1 in terms of all the other unknowns.*

4. *Substitute this expression for z_1 wherever it occurs in the other equations.* This gives $n - 1$ equations in $n - 1$ unknowns. The equation from step 3 is reserved until the end to evaluate z_1.

5. *Repeat this sequence* of steps 1 through 4 until only one equation in one unknown remains. Solve this for the numerical value which is consistent with the conditions of the problem. The final equation may have negative or imaginary roots; these cannot represent physical quantities such as concentrations. It may have several positive real roots, but usually only one of these will give positive values for all the other unknowns.

---

* Avoid the use of x as an unknown when the numbers in the equation are expressed in exponential form: 1.19×10^5. It is very easy to confuse the unknown with a multiplication sign.

6. *Substitute back.* When the last equation has been solved, its root is substituted back in the equations obtained in step 3 to obtain values for all the other unknowns.

7. *Check the answers.* The numerical answers are then checked by substituting in the original set of equations to see if they are all satisfied.

In simple problems, the final equation may be linear or quadratic, but, if most problems are solved exactly, the final equation may be of fifth or sixth degree or even higher. Solving higher-degree equations numerically is quite feasible, and the easiest method is to plot a graph of the function and find where the curve crosses the axis. However, we would like to avoid this if possible, hence we make as many simplifying approximations as we can before we set about solving the simultaneous equations. Since these approximations vary with the chemical nature of the system that we are dealing with, they will be discussed in later chapters. Here we shall give an example of the exact solution of a set of simultaneous equations.

Example 1. In a problem involving a weak acid HA in water, the following simultaneous equations are obtained*:

$$[H^+][A^-] = K_a[HA] \tag{1}$$

$$[H^+] = [A^-] \tag{2}$$

$$[HA] + [A^-] = C \tag{3}$$

Here K_a is the ionization constant of the weak acid, and C is the analytical (total) concentration of acid in water. The formulas enclosed in square brackets represent the concentrations in moles/liter of the various species at equilibrium.

Consider these equations now as a mathematical problem in which K_a and C are given, and $[H^+]$, $[A^-]$, and $[HA]$ are unknown concentrations to be found. We have three simultaneous equations in three unknowns. The first equation is *nonlinear* since it involves the product of two concentrations, so that the only straightforward method of solving these three equations is by *substitution*.

The unknown $[A^-]$ occurs in all three equations, $[H^+]$ occurs in two, and $[HA]$ occurs in two. We shall choose to eliminate $[HA]$ first since we would probably be most interested in $[H^+]$ if we were actually solving the problem. Solving Eq. (3) for $[HA]$, we get

$$[HA] = C - [A^-]. \tag{4}$$

From Eq. (2) we have

$$[A^-] = [H^+]. \tag{5}$$

---

*Square brackets around the formula of a species represents its concentration in moles/liter (or gram-ions/liter). The chemistry of weak acid systems is discussed in detail in Section 4-1. Here we are dealing with a purely mathematical example.

Substituting both these equations in (1) gives

$$[H^+]^2 = K_a(C - [H^+]). \tag{6}$$

Knowing the values of K_a and C, we can solve the quadratic equation (6) for $[H^+]$ using the methods which we shall describe in the next section, but which may already be familiar to you. Once the value of $[H^+]$ is known, we obtain $[A^-]$ by substituting in Eq. (5); and $[HA]$ by substituting in Eq. (4). Thus all the unknown concentrations can be obtained.

1–2 QUADRATIC EQUATIONS

A second-degree or quadratic equation can be solved algebraically, and the general solution is taught in most high-school algebra courses. However, blind use of the quadratic formula sometimes leads to awkward and inaccurate results, so that it is often easier and more accurate to solve a quadratic equation by successive approximations. We shall discuss both methods here.

The quadratic formula.   The general solution of the equation

$$az^2 + bz + c = 0 \tag{1}$$

is

$$z = \frac{-b \pm \sqrt{b^2 - 4ac}}{2a}, \tag{2}$$

and, in principle, all one needs to do to solve any quadratic equation is to put it into the form of Eq. (1), identify the coefficients a, b, and c, and substitute these in Eq. (2). In many cases this yields an answer of the desired accuracy.

Example 2.   Solve the quadratic equation $4.7z(z + 0.66) = 17$. This may be cast into the form of Eq. (1):

$$4.7z^2 + 3.1z - 17 = 0.$$

By comparing with Eq. (1), we identify

$$a = 4.7, \qquad b = 3.1, \qquad c = -17.$$

Substituting in Eq. (2), we have

$$z = \frac{-3.1 \pm \sqrt{9.6 + 319.6}}{9.4} = +1.60 \quad \text{or} \quad -2.26.$$

Only the positive root has any physical meaning, so we take

$$z = 1.60.$$

Successive approximations. In contrast, considerable difficulty may be encountered if the quadratic formula is used on some other equations. If the term $4ac$ is small compared to b^2, the square root in Eq. (2) will be nearly equal to b, and finding the positive real root will involve taking the difference of two nearly equal numbers. Under such circumstances, a very large number of significant figures may be required for the square root to obtain an answer of the desired accuracy. A much simpler way to approach the problem in such a case is to use successive approximations.

Example 3. Solve the quadratic equation

$$z^2 + 345z - 563 = 0. \tag{3}$$

Substitution in the quadratic formula [Eq. (2)] gives

$$z = \frac{-345 \pm \sqrt{1.190 \times 10^{+5} + 2.252 \times 10^{+3}}}{2}$$

$$= \frac{-345 \pm 348}{2} = -346 \quad \text{or} \quad +1.5.$$

Even though the calculations were carried out to three significant figures, the positive root is accurate to only about 30% because it is the difference of two nearly equal numbers.

A brute-force approach would be to calculate the square root more accurately by using seven-place logarithms, but a more clever approach is to realize that for the positive root, the term z^2 in Eq. (3) is rather small compared with either of the other terms. If we cast the original equation (3) in the form

$$345z = 563 - z^2,$$

$$z = 1.632 - 2.90 \times 10^{-3}z^2, \tag{4}$$

we see that any reasonable assumption for the value of z^2 on the right-hand side of Eq. (4) yields a value of z which is only slightly different from 1.632.

If we assume that z is approximately zero for our first approximation and set $z^2 = 0$ on the right-hand side of Eq. (4), we find that for our second approximation $z = 1.632$. Substituting this value for z on the right-hand side of Eq. (4) again, we obtain for our third approximation

$$z = 1.632 - 0.008 = 1.624.$$

A fourth approximation gives the same answer to four significant figures.

Rules for solving quadratic equations. Only when the quadratic term is small does trouble arise in using the quadratic formula, so we can make the following rules for solving any quadratic equation.

1. *One positive real root* always exists for Eq. (1), if a and b are positive but c is negative. Most equations we shall encounter are of this type.

2. *Use the quadratic formula*, Eq. (2), only when $4ac$ is greater than 10% of b^2.

3. *Use successive approximations* if $4ac$ is smaller than 10% of b^2. Under these conditions, blind use of the quadratic formula may lead to considerable error, and it is better to use successive approximations. To do this, cast the equation in the form

$$z = -\frac{c}{b} - \frac{a}{b} z^2, \qquad (5)$$

and note that the term $(-c/b)$ is a positive number because c is assumed to be negative. Assume that $z = 0$ on the right-hand side of Eq. (5) for the first approximation. Continue making approximations, as in Example 3, until two successive approximations agree to within the desired limit of error.

1–3 LOGARITHMIC FUNCTIONS

It is common practice in the chemistry of ionic solutions to use logarithmic functions of concentrations, particularly $[H^+]$. There are several reasons for this. First, the electrochemical potentials by which concentrations are measured experimentally vary with the logarithm of the concentration. Second, the concentrations encountered in practice vary from 10 down to 10^{-15} moles/liter, and any graphical representation of their variation must be logarithmic simply to cover the wide range of values. Third, logarithmic plots often reduce the equations relating concentrations to straight lines or slight curves, and in many cases calculations can be made directly with the graphs. Examples of graphical calculations are given in Chapter 4.

Definition of pH. Because the concentrations of solutions are nearly always less than one mole/liter, the logarithm of the concentration is nearly always a negative number. Because people prefer working with positive numbers between 1 and 10, hydrogen ion concentration is usually expressed as pH, given in dilute solution by the approximate relation*

$$pH = -\log_{10}[H^+].$$

---

* A rigorous definition of pH is quite difficult to come by. In theory it is defined to be the negative logarithm of the activity (concentration corrected for interionic forces) of hydrogen ion: $pH = -\log_{10} [H^+]\gamma_{H^+}$, but the activity coefficient γ_{H^+} of a single ion cannot be measured experimentally. In practice, the form of the pH function is assumed to be that measured by a pH meter, and the meter is calibrated at several points by using standard buffer solutions. These standard buffers are assumed to have their theoretically calculated pH values.

Thus a solution with a hydrogen ion concentration of 1.0×10^{-5} mole/liter has pH $= 5.00$. Because of the errors inherent in the practical pH scale, values of pH are rarely accurate to better than ± 0.01, which corresponds to $\pm 2\%$ in $[H^+]$.

Other logarithmic functions. Other logarithmic functions are also defined by analogy, the lower-case p being an abbreviation for "take the negative logarithm of . . ." Common ones encountered are

$$pOH = -\log_{10} [OH^-],$$
$$pAg = -\log_{10} [Ag^+],$$
$$pCl = -\log_{10} [Cl^-],$$
$$pK_a = -\log_{10} K_a, \quad \text{etc.}$$

Converting $[H^+]$ to pH. Converting from $[H^+]$ to pH and the reverse often causes mistakes in calculations, and the following step-by-step reasoning is recommended for decreasing the probability of error.

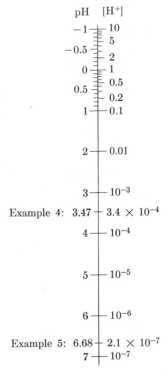

Example 4. Find the pH of a solution with $[H^+] = 3.4 \times 10^{-4}$.

$$pH = -\log [H^+]$$
$$= -\log (3.4 \times 10^{-4})$$
$$= -\log 3.4 - \log 10^{-4}$$
$$= 4 - \log 3.4$$
$$= 4.00 - 0.53$$
$$pH = 3.47.$$

Note that 3.47 is between 3 and 4, and that 3.4×10^{-4} is between 10^{-3} and 10^{-4}. This is shown in the scale of Fig. 1–1. A simple qualitative check like this will prevent the error of a factor of 100 which is commonly made.

Example 5. Find K_a for an acid with $pK_a = 6.68$.

$$pK_a = -\log K_a,$$
$$\log K_a = -6.68,$$
$$\log K_a = -7.00 + 0.32,$$
$$K_a = (\text{antilog } 0.32) \times 10^{-7},$$
$$K_a = 2.1 \times 10^{-7}.$$

Again note that 6.68 is between 6 and 7, and that K_a is between 10^{-6} and 10^{-7}.

FIG. 1–1. Scale showing the relation between pH and hydrogen ion concentration, or between pK_a and K_a.

Using a slide rule for logarithmic functions. The conversion from pH to $[H^+]$ and vice versa might be done with less chance of making a mistake if a large-scale version of Fig. 1–1 is used. Such a scale is found on any slide rule, and the calculations may be made as follows.

To calculate pH from $[H^+]$, when $[H^+]$ is smaller than one mole/liter, make the part of the pH to the left of the decimal point one *less* in magnitude than the exponent of 10 in $[H^+]$. To find the part of the pH to the right of the decimal point, align the slide index (C-scale) with the fixed index (D-scale), set the pre-exponential* factor on the CI-scale and read the decimal part of the pH on the L-scale.

With slide rules where the L-scale is on the back, turn the slide over so that the zero end of the L-scale is lined up with the 9.99-end of the D-scale. Then the pre-exponential factor is set on the D-scale, and the decimal part of the pH is read on the L-scale.

Example 6. Find pH, given that $[H^+] = 3.4 \times 10^{-4}$. The part of the pH to the left of the decimal point is 1 *less* than 4, that is, 3:

$$pH = 3.\underline{\quad}.$$

Set the C- and D-scales together. Set 3.4 on the CI-scale and read 0.47 on the L-scale:

$$pH = 3.47.$$

To find $[H^+]$ from pH, reverse the process. The negative exponent of 10 is the next integer *higher* than the pH. The pre-exponential factor is read on the CI-scale when the decimal part of the pH is set on the L-scale.

Example 7. Find $[H^+]$, given that pH $= 5.27$. The negative exponent of 10 is the next integer *higher* than the pH, that is, -6:

$$[H^+] = \underline{\quad} \times 10^{-6}.$$

Set the C- and D-scales together. Set 0.27 on the L-scale and read 5.4 on the CI-scale:

$$[H^+] = 5.4 \times 10^{-6}.$$

---

* The pre-exponential factor is the number before the power of ten. In the number 2.1×10^{-7}, 2.1 is the pre-exponential factor.

PROBLEMS

The following sets of simultaneous equations were obtained in the course of equilibrium calculations. Solve them for all the unknowns. Check to see if your answers satisfy the original equations within $\pm 5\%$.

1. $[Pb^{++}][IO_3^-]^2 = 2.6 \times 10^{-13}$
    $S = [Pb^{++}]$
    $2S = [IO_3^-]$. (S means solubility. See Chapter 2.)

2. $[Ba^{++}][SO_4^=] = 1.0 \times 10^{-10}$
    $[Ba^{++}] = 1.0 \times 10^{-2} + [SO_4^=]$

3. $[Ag^+][Cl^-] = 1.8 \times 10^{-10}$
    $[Ag^+] = 1.0 \times 10^{-7} + [Cl^-]$

4. $[H^+][CN^-] = 4.8 \times 10^{-10}[HCN]$
    $[H^+][OH^-] = 1.0 \times 10^{-14}$
    $[H^+] = [CN^-] + [OH^-]$
    $[HCN] = 1.0 \times 10^{-4}$

5. $[H^+][CN^-] = 4.8 \times 10^{-10}[HCN]$
    $[H^+][OH^-] = 1.0 \times 10^{-14}$
    $[HCN] = [OH^-]$
    $[CN^-] = 1.0 \times 10^{-2}$

6. $[HgOH^+][H^+] = 2.0 \times 10^{-4}[Hg^{++}]$
    $[H^+] = 10.4[HgOH^+]$
    $[Hg^{++}] + [HgOH^+] = 9.76 \times 10^{-3}$

Solve the following quadratic equations.

7. $7.3 \times 10^{-5}[Cl^-](1 + 3.3 \times 10^{+3}[Cl^-]) = 4.4 \times 10^{-2}$

8. $1.8 \times 10^{-4}[NH_3]^2 + 3.6 \times 10^{-8}[NH_3] - 5.5 \times 10^{-14} = 0.66 \times 10^{-16}$

9. Find the pH of solutions with the following concentrations of H^+.
    (a) 6.4×10^{-3} (b) 1.3×10^{-7}
    (c) 4.3×10^{-9} (d) 9.2×10^{-1}
    (e) 4.65 (f) 7.7×10^{-10}
    (g) 2.3×10^{-2} (h) 6.5×10^{-14}
    (i) 9.1×10^{-15} (j) 4.35×10^{-5}

10. In a table, the solubility products of salts are given as pK_{s0}. Find K_{s0}.
    (a) 10.43 (b) 32.45
    (c) 41.3 (d) 6.54

11. If $[H^+][OH^-] = 1.0 \times 10^{-14}$, find the relation between pH and pOH.

12. Under certain conditions, a buffer consisting of a weak acid with ionization constant K_a and its salt, in the ratio R, has a hydrogen ion concentration given by $[H^+] = K_a R$. Express pH and pOH as functions of pK_a and $\log R$, using the result of problem 11.

Solubility | 2

I stood at the bottom of the crack and watched my friend climb. His movements were apparently so effortless that it was hard to remember that he was holding himself on to a vertical wall by jamming his hands and feet into the same crack. He disappeared out of sight round a bulge, and I heard the ringing of his hammer as he drove a piton into a crack in the solid rock. "It's your turn now," he called, "a rather nice climb." I tried to wedge my boot in the crack so that it wouldn't be too hard to get it out again, and felt with my hand for something to hang on to.

2–1 THE SOLUBILITY PRODUCT

In 1899, W. Nernst, one of the founders of modern physical chemistry, showed by measuring the solubility of silver acetate in sodium acetate solutions that the solubility of ionic salts in water or in dilute solutions of other salts was governed by the solubility product expression. Although this was not the first equilibrium expression to be discovered, it is in many ways the simplest, and provides a convenient starting point for our discussion.

The solubility product expression may be stated in general as follows: For a dilute aqueous solution *saturated* with the salt M_zX_y, the concentrations* of the cation M^{+y} and the anion X^{-z} obey the equation

$$[M^{+y}]^z[X^{-z}]^y = K_{s0} \tag{1}$$

regardless of whether the ions come from the salt with which the solution is saturated or from other salts which are added to the solution. As usual, the square brackets around the formula of a species indicate the concentration of that species in moles/liter of solution. K_{s0} is called the *solubility product constant*.† It depends on temperature, but it is nearly independent

---

* Rigorously, these should be activities. See Section 2–4.

† The symbol K_{s0} is used in this book instead of K_{sp} or K_s, in order to conform with the notation approved by the International Union of Pure and Applied Chemistry. This notation is used in the IUPAC tables of *Stability Constants*. (See the appendix for reference.)

11

of the concentrations of the various ions provided that the solution is rather dilute. K_{s0} is also nearly constant if a fairly large and constant concentration of some salt such as KNO_3 or $NaClO_4$, whose ions do not react with the ions being studied, is present (see Section 2-4). The solubility products of a number of salts which, when dissolved in water, yield only two ions in appreciable concentrations, are listed in the appendix.

Experimental verification of solubility product relation. Since it is unreasonable to expect you to accept the fact that the solubility product relation holds, without providing some evidence, let us consider the results of an actual experiment designed to measure the solubility product of silver bromate, $AgBrO_3$. In this experiment, solutions containing potassium bromate and potassium nitrate were saturated with silver bromate. The total concentration of potassium bromate and potassium nitrate was the same for all samples, but different relative amounts of potassium bromate were used in order to change the concentration of bromate ion without changing the total ionic concentration.

The various samples were held in a thermostat at 25°C and shaken periodically, so that eventually equilibrium was reached between the solid and the solution. Then each solution was separated from the solid by filtration, and the solution was analyzed for its silver content by titrating it with potassium thiocyanate. The results of such an experiment are listed in Table 2-1 and are shown graphically in Fig. 2-1.

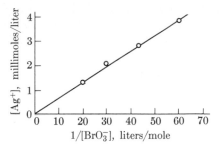

FIG. 2-1. Verification of the solubility product law for silver bromate. Circles are experimental measurements. The straight line corresponds to a solubility product $K_{s0} = 6.5 \times 10^{-5}$.

The method of plotting the data may seem a bit peculiar, but it is really quite reasonable. The solubility product expression for a solution saturated with silver bromate, according to the general form (1), is

$$[Ag^+][BrO_3^-] = K_{s0}, \tag{2}$$

and hence we would expect the concentration of silver ion in the saturated solution to vary inversely with the concentration of bromate ion according to the relation

$$[Ag^+] = K_{s0} \frac{1}{[BrO_3^-]}. \tag{3}$$

TABLE 2–1

DATA FOR DETERMINING THE SOLUBILITY PRODUCT OF SILVER BROMATE

$[\text{BrO}_3^-]$ moles/liter	$[\text{Ag}^+]$ moles/liter	$[\text{Ag}^+][\text{BrO}_3^-] = K_{s0}$ (moles/liter)^2
5.00×10^{-2}	1.28×10^{-3}	6.40×10^{-5}
3.33×10^{-2}	2.02×10^{-3}	6.72×10^{-5}
2.27×10^{-2}	2.84×10^{-3}	6.45×10^{-5}
1.67×10^{-2}	3.85×10^{-3}	$\underline{6.44 \times 10^{-5}}$
	Average K_{s0}	6.50×10^{-5}
	Average deviation	$\pm 0.1 \times 10^{-5}$

If we plot the measured concentrations of silver ion as a function of the reciprocal concentrations of bromate ion, we should obtain a series of points falling on a straight line through the origin of the graph. If you look at Fig. 2–1, you will see that this is indeed true.

One point concerning the way the graph is plotted: You will note that the sizes of the scales used for the two axes are quite different. On the vertical scale $[\text{Ag}^+]$ is plotted in millimoles/liter. This means that one large unit on this scale corresponds to 1×10^{-3} mole/liter in $[\text{Ag}^+]$. On the horizontal scale $1/[\text{BrO}_3^-]$ is plotted in liters/mole. This means that the reciprocal of $[\text{BrO}_3^-]$ in moles/liter was used to plot the scale. The numerical data used to plot the points is listed in Table 2–1.

Note that the points do not fall precisely on the straight line, but seem to cluster about it. An unsophisticated but very careful worker might be tempted to draw an S-shaped curve through the points. We did not do this because we had a strong theoretical reason to believe that the points should fall on a straight line. We also know that there are many errors in weighing out samples, measuring volumes, keeping the temperature constant, achieving true equilibrium, making sure that all the precipitate was filtered out, and titrating to the correct end point. Thus we can reasonably ascribe the observed deviations from the straight line to experimental error.

Finally, we can obtain the value of the solubility product from the graph in Fig. 2–1. We drew a straight line through this set of points and made it go through the origin because we expected Eq. (3) to hold. According to Eq. (3), the slope of the straight line is equal to the solubility product K_{s0}. To find this slope, we take any point on the line, read off the value of $[\text{Ag}^+]$ and the value of $1/[\text{BrO}_3^-]$, divide the first by the second, and obtain the value of K_{s0}. The equation of the straight line is

$$[Ag^+][BrO_3^-] = 6.5 \times 10^{-5}$$

and the value of the solubility product is 6.5×10^{-5} (mole/liter)^2.

Alternatively, we could obtain a number of independent measurements of K_{s0} from the original data, as shown in Table 2–1. The average of the four results is taken to be the value of the solubility product:

$$K_{s0} = (6.5 \pm 0.1) \times 10^{-5}.$$

The advantage of the numerical method is that it provides a quantitative estimate of the uncertainty in the constant. The advantage of the graphical method is that it displays all the data in a single picture, and lets us see at a glance that the theoretical relation is in fact obeyed.

2–2 SOLUBILITY OF SALTS IN PURE WATER

Many ionic salts dissolve in pure water to yield only two ions of appreciable concentration. If the saturated solution is not so concentrated that interionic forces are appreciable, it is possible to calculate the solubility of the salt from its solubility product alone.

To perform this calculation, we must relate the solubility of the salt to the individual ionic concentrations which appear in the solubility product expression. This relation is provided by the mass balance on each of the ions. If S moles of silver bromate dissolve in pure water to form a liter of saturated solution, then a mass balance on silver is simply

$$[Ag^+] = S. \tag{1}$$

This mass balance states that all the silver which dissolves in the solution is present exclusively as Ag^+. No complexes are formed with bromate ion and no appreciable amount of AgOH or solid Ag_2O is formed by reaction of the silver ion with water. Similarly, if there is no source of bromate ion other than the silver bromate which dissolves, and all the bromate ion that dissolves is present in that form, a mass balance on the bromate group is simply

$$[BrO_3^-] = S. \tag{2}$$

As we saw in the previous section, in any solution saturated with silver bromate, the solubility product relation

$$[Ag^+][BrO_3^-] = K_{s0} \tag{3}$$

is obeyed at equilibrium. These three simultaneous equations in three unknowns may be combined to give

$$S = \sqrt{K_{s0}}. \tag{4}$$

Thus the solubility of an ionic salt in pure water depends on the solubility product alone, provided that only these two ions are in solution.

If the charges on the ions are not equal, the solubility is still determined by the solubility product alone, but the equations are slightly more complicated. For the general salt M_zX_y, which yields only the ions M^{+y} and X^{-z} in solution in pure water, we may represent the solution process as a chemical reaction

$$M_zX_y(s) \rightleftharpoons z\,M^{+y} + y\,X^{-z},$$

where (s) means that the substance is present as a solid. The equilibrium constant for this reaction is the solubility product:

$$[M^{+y}]^z[X^{-z}]^y = K_{s0},$$

which we stated in the previous section. Since each mole of salt that dissolves gives z moles of cations and y moles of anions, the mass balances are

$$[M^{+y}] = zS, \qquad [X^{-z}] = yS.$$

Substitution of the mass balances in the solubility product gives

$$(zS)^z(yS)^y = K_{s0},$$

which may be easily solved for S in terms of the known quantities z, y, and K_{s0}:

$$S = \sqrt[z+y]{K_{s0}/z^zy^y}.$$

Let us now consider a few numerical examples.

Example 1. Calculate the solubility product of barium sulfate, knowing that its solubility in pure water determined by conductivity measurements at 25°C is 1.05×10^{-5} mole/liter. The mass balances give

$$[Ba^{++}] = 1.05 \times 10^{-5}, \qquad [SO_4^=] = 1.05 \times 10^{-5}.$$

Substitution in the solubility product relation gives

$$K_{s0} = [Ba^{++}][SO_4^=] = (1.05 \times 10^{-5})^2 = 1.10 \times 10^{-10}.$$

Example 2. The solubility product of CaF_2 is 4.0×10^{-11}. Calculate the solubility of calcium fluoride in pure water. The solubility product expression for calcium fluoride is

$$[Ca^{++}][F^-]^2 = 4.0 \times 10^{-11}.$$

The mass balances are

$$[Ca^{++}] = S, \qquad [F^-] = 2S.$$

Substituting in the solubility product, we have

$$S(2S)^2 = 4.0 \times 10^{-11},$$

$$4S^3 = 4.0 \times 10^{-11},$$

$$S^3 = 1.0 \times 10^{-11},$$

$$S = 2.2 \times 10^{-4} \text{ mole/liter}.$$

This is 1.7×10^{-2} gm/liter, which agrees favorably with a typical direct solubility measurement giving 1.6×10^{-2} gm/liter, even though we have not considered the effects of ionic strength or side reactions (Sections 2–4 and 2–5).

2–3 THE COMMON ION EFFECT

In a saturated solution of an ionic salt such as $BaSO_4$, the concentration of the ions is governed by the solubility product relation

$$[Ba^{++}][SO_4^=] = K_{s0},$$

even if other salts are dissolved in the solution. If the concentration of one of the ions is increased by the addition of $BaCl_2$ or Na_2SO_4, the concentration of the other must be decreased or the equilibrium will not be maintained. That is, the addition of a common ion results in a decrease in the solubility of the salt, provided no complex ions are formed in appreciable concentrations (see Section 2–5). This is easily seen in the numerical examples.

Example 3. Calculate the solubility of $BaSO_4$ in 1.0×10^{-2} molar $BaCl_2$. The solubility-product expression is

$$[Ba^{++}][SO_4^=] = 1.1 \times 10^{-10}$$

at 25°C. The mass balances are

$$[SO_4^=] = S, \qquad [Ba^{++}] = S + 1.0 \times 10^{-2}.$$

Note that the barium in solution comes from both the $BaSO_4$ which dissolves

(S), and the added $BaCl_2$ (1.0×10^{-2}). When the mass balances are substituted in the solubility product, we get

$$S(S + 1.0 \times 10^{-2}) = 1.1 \times 10^{-10}.$$

The solubility of $BaSO_4$ in pure water is about 10^{-5} mole/liter (Example 1), and its solubility in a $BaCl_2$ solution will be even less, so that we can neglect S compared to 1.0×10^{-2} in the above equation. This gives simply

$$S = 1.1 \times 10^{-8},$$

which is indeed negligible, being one-millionth of 10^{-2}. Thus we see that the presence of a common ion reduces the solubility quite extensively.

Let us now consider the general problem of the solubility of a salt in solutions containing a common ion. For simplicity, we shall restrict ourselves to salts where cation and anion have equal charges, and for concreteness, let us call the salt $BaSO_4$ and the common ion $SO_4^=$. Of course, the results apply to any one-to-one salt when side reactions which form other species are negligible.

The mass balances are

$$[Ba^{++}] = S, \tag{1}$$

$$[SO_4^=] = S + C, \tag{2}$$

where S is the molar solubility of $BaSO_4$ and C is the analytical concentration of sulfate, which is the amount of sodium sulfate added to the solution. On substituting (1) and (2) in the solubility product

$$[Ba^{++}][SO_4^=] = K_{s0}, \tag{3}$$

we get

$$S(S + C) = K_{s0}. \tag{4}$$

If a large excess of common ion is present, as in Example 3, S can be neglected compared to C, which gives simply

$$S = \frac{K_{s0}}{C}, \qquad \text{approximately.}$$

If only a small excess of sulfate is present, however, neither of the terms within the brackets is negligible, and the quadratic [Eq. (4)] must be solved.

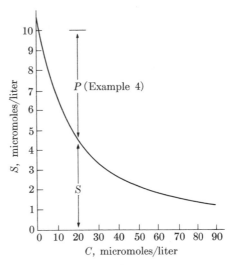

Fig. 2–2. Solubility of $BaSO_4$ in Na_2SO_4 solutions of analytical concentration C. The quantities P and S refer to Example 4.

Figure 2–2 shows the solubility of $BaSO_4$ in Na_2SO_4 solutions of analytical concentration C in the region where S is *not* negligible compared to C. The curve was plotted by assuming values for S and calculating C from (4) with $K_{s0} = 1.1 \times 10^{-10}$.

Mixing two solutions.   Let us now consider an example where two solutions are mixed and a salt precipitates. Unless the two solutions are in exactly the stoichiometric ratio, the common ion effect will decrease the solubility of the salt and make the precipitation more complete.

Example 4.   50 ml of a solution containing 3.0×10^{-5} mole $BaCl_2$ per liter are mixed with 100 ml of a solution containing 4.5×10^{-5} mole Na_2SO_4 per liter. Calculate the fraction of barium precipitated as $BaSO_4$.

Let P be the number of moles of $BaSO_4$ precipitated per liter of solution. Then the mass balances can be expressed in the form

$$[Ba^{++}] + P = 3.0 \times 10^{-5} \left(\frac{50}{150} \right) = 1.0 \times 10^{-5}, \tag{5}$$

$$[SO_4^=] + P = 4.5 \times 10^{-5} \left(\frac{100}{150} \right) = 3.0 \times 10^{-5}, \tag{6}$$

where the concentrations given have been corrected for dilution. Note that three times the amount of sulfate theoretically required to react with all the barium has been added. The above equations, together with the solubility product

$$[Ba^{++}][SO_4^=] = 1.1 \times 10^{-10}, \tag{3}$$

provide three equations in three unknowns. Subtracting (5) from (6) to eliminate P gives

$$[Ba^{++}] + 2.0 \times 10^{-5} = [SO_4^=]. \tag{7}$$

Substituting $[SO_4^=]$ from (7) in (3) gives a quadratic for $[Ba^{++}]$

$$[Ba^{++}]^2 + 2.0 \times 10^{-5}[Ba^{++}] - 1.1 \times 10^{-10} = 0,$$

which may be solved by the quadratic formula to yield

$$[Ba^{++}] = 4.5 \times 10^{-6}.$$

From (5) we then have

$$P = 5.5 \times 10^{-6}.$$

Since the total amount of barium was 1.0×10^{-5} mole/liter after dilution, 55% of the barium has been precipitated. The solubility of $BaSO_4$ in water is slightly greater than 1.0×10^{-5}, therefore if it were not for the excess sulfate added, we would have had no precipitate at all.

As can be seen from Fig. 2–2, this problem is closely related to the problem of finding the solubility of $BaSO_4$ in 2.0×10^{-5} molar Na_2SO_4. This concentration is the excess sulfate concentration over that required to react with all the barium present if precipitation were complete. Note that if S is eliminated between (1) and (2), with $C = 2.0 \times 10^{-5}$, we obtain

$$[Ba^{++}] + 2.0 \times 10^{-5} = [SO_4^=],$$

which is identical to (7). P is the difference between the total concentration of barium (1.0×10^{-5} mole/liter) and the solubility $S = [Ba^{++}] = 4.5 \times 10^{-6}$ mole/liter. Thus Eq. (5) may be written:

$$S + P = 1.0 \times 10^{-5}.$$

Whether a precipitation problem is formulated in terms of S or P is a matter of taste, and usually depends on the way the problem is stated.

Separation of compounds by precipitation. One of the oldest methods of chemical separation is fractional precipitation. This involves the addition of a reagent which precipitates most of one metal ion and leaves another mostly in solution. Simple calculations based on equilibrium constants can tell the maximum degree of separation which can be achieved under given conditions. Example 5 below is a typical calculation.

In practice, the separation will be poorer than calculated due to *coprecipitation*. In this phenomenon are included the mechanical enclosure of some solution by the precipitate, adsorption of foreign ions on the surface of the precipitate, solid solution formation, etc. Such a discussion is beyond the scope of this book, and we shall not consider these points further.

Example 5. A solution is 0.010 molar in $BaCl_2$ and 0.010 molar in $SrCl_2$. Concentrated sodium sulfate solution is added to the solution. Which ion precipitates first? What is its concentration when the second ion begins to precipitate?

Two solubility products are involved, each holding *only* in the presence of the corresponding solid salt:

$$[Ba^{++}][SO_4^=] = 1.1 \times 10^{-10}, \tag{1}$$

$$[Sr^{++}][SO_4^=] = 2.8 \times 10^{-7}. \tag{2}$$

In a solution in equilibrium with both solids, dividing (2) by (1) shows that $[Sr^{++}]$ is much larger than $[Ba^{++}]$:

$$\frac{[Sr^{++}]}{[Ba^{++}]} = 2.5 \times 10^{+3}. \tag{3}$$

When the first crystal of $SrSO_4$ precipitates, we see from (3) that $[Ba^{++}]$ is less than one-thousandth as large as [Sr^{++}], the rest of the barium having precipitated as BaSO$_4$. Thus BaSO$_4$ precipitates first.

When SrSO$_4$ first starts to precipitate, neglecting dilution,

$$[Sr^{++}] = 0.010.$$

From (3)

$$[Ba^{++}] = 4.0 \times 10^{-6}.$$

When any sulfate in excess of the amount required to start precipitation of Sr^{++} has been added, (3) will hold, and the composition of the solution will remain unchanged as SrSO$_4$ and BaSO$_4$ precipitate together. The optimum separation will be obtained if exactly the stoichiometric amount of sulfate required to precipitate all the barium is added. At this point, the solid is in principle pure BaSO$_4$ (in practice coprecipitation occurs), and the concentrations in the saturated solution are as given above. Only about 0.04% Ba^{++} remains to contaminate Sr^{++} in the solution. No further purification of the solution can be accomplished by this method unless the solution is made more concentrated.

In gravimetric analysis, this method of separating Sr^{++} and Ba^{++} is not useful unless some method can be found to prevent precipitation of SrSO$_4$. One possibility is to use such dilute solutions that the saturation point for SrSO$_4$ is never reached (see Problem 30) or to use some other precipitating reagent. A popular method is to precipitate strontium and barium as chromates, varying the acidity and adding alcohol to the solution to make the solubility difference larger. About 0.5% error is claimed for this gravimetric method. It is more common to analyze mixtures whose ions are so difficult to separate by some more specific method. In the case of barium and strontium, flame photometry is the most useful method, giving results accurate to about 1% under favorable conditions.

2–4 THE EFFECT OF IONIC STRENGTH

According to the solubility-product relation, the solubility of a salt should be unaffected by the addition of a salt having no ions in common with it, and no ions that react with its ions. This is not in fact the case. Figure 2–3 shows the solubility of silver iodate in solutions containing added potassium iodate and potassium nitrate. As is predicted by the solubility-product law, the solubility of silver iodate in potassium iodate solutions decreases to a great extent as the concentration of potassium iodate is increased. However, the solubility of silver iodate in solutions of potassium nitrate is seen to increase, not remain constant, as the concentration of potassium nitrate is increased. This increase is a result of the interionic forces resulting from the addition of extraneous ions to the solution, even though no chemical reaction occurs between the ions of potassium nitrate and those of silver iodate, once the salts are dissolved in water.

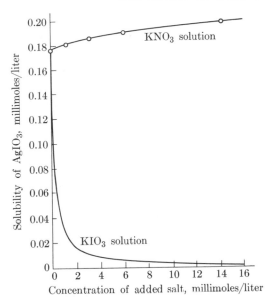

FIG. 2–3.   Effect of added salt on the solubility of AgIO₃.
The circles are experimental points obtained in potassium nitrate
solutions. The curve for potassium iodate solutions was calculated
from the solubility product of silver iodate.

In accordance with these observations, the solubility-product law may
be stated more rigorously as follows:

$$K_{s0}^0 = \{Ag^+\}\{IO_3^-\} = [Ag^+][IO_3^-]\gamma_+\gamma_-, \tag{1}$$

where the activity of the silver ion $\{Ag^+\}$ is set equal to its concentration
times an *activity coefficient* γ_+, which corrects for the interionic forces,
and the activity of the iodate ion $\{IO_3^-\}$ is written as the product of its
concentration and an activity coefficient γ_-. In very dilute solutions,
the activity approaches the concentration, and the activity coefficients become unity.

Experimentally, we can determine only the product $\gamma_+\gamma_-$ since we
cannot isolate individual ions, but must always deal with electrically
neutral solutions. Therefore, the activity coefficients of salt solutions are
given as the geometric mean

$$\gamma_\pm = \sqrt{\gamma_+\gamma_-}.$$

This mean activity coefficient is found to depend on the total *ionic strength*
I of the solution, defined to be

$$I = \tfrac{1}{2}\sum_i C_i z_i^2. \tag{2}$$

That is, the concentration C_i of each ion (i) is multiplied by the square of its charge z_i, all the terms for the various ions in solution are added together, and half the resultant is the ionic strength. For a simple salt like KNO_3, the ionic strength is equal to its concentration:

$$I = \tfrac{1}{2}([K^+](1)^2 + [NO_3^-](-1)^2),$$

but since $[K^+] = [NO_3^-] = C$, the concentration of the salt, we have

$$I = C.$$

For the mixture of potassium nitrate and silver iodate, the ionic strength is the sum of the concentrations of the two salts:

$$I = \tfrac{1}{2}([K^+] + [NO_3^-] + [Ag^+] + [IO_3^-]),$$

$$I = C_{KNO_3} + C_{AgIO_3}.$$

Thus by adding various amounts of potassium nitrate to saturated silver iodate solutions, the ionic strength of the solution is varied at will.

Experimental measurement of activity coefficient. You will recall that in the measurement of the solubility product of silver bromate, which we discussed in Section 2–1, potassium nitrate was added so that the total concentration of salts in the solution was constant. Since all the salts concerned produced ions of unit charge, this also meant that the ionic strength, and hence the activity coefficients, were kept constant. This was why we observed the solubility product relation to hold so well.

The activity coefficient $\gamma_\pm$ can be calculated as follows: The measured solubilties are extrapolated* (Fig. 2–4) to zero ionic strength, where $\gamma_\pm = 1$, giving a value of

$$S_0 = 1.733 \times 10^{-4} \text{ mole/liter}$$

for the solubility at zero ionic strength. The thermodynamic (activity) solubility product is calculated from this solubility to be

$$K_{s0}^0 = S_0^2 = 3.00 \times 10^{-8} \text{ mole/liter}^2.$$

Then the mean activity coefficient is calculated at each concentration

---

* According to the Debye-Hückel theory, the best extrapolation should be obtained if $\log S$ is plotted as a function of $\sqrt{I}$. Because the range of S is so small, however, it makes little difference, in this case, whether S or $\log S$ is plotted.

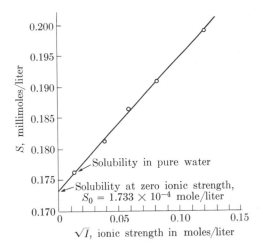

FIG. 2–4.   Extrapolation of solubility to zero ionic strength. The circles are the same experimental points as those plotted in Fig. 2–3.

from the measured solubility S by means of relation (1):

$$\gamma_{\pm}^2 = \gamma_+\gamma_- = \frac{K_{s0}^0}{[Ag^+][IO_3^-]} = \frac{K_{s0}^0}{S^2}. \tag{3}$$

These activity coefficients are plotted in Figs. 2–5 and 2–6 as a function of the ionic strength. The measured values of $\gamma_{\pm}$ are fitted quite closely by the equation predicted by the Debye-Hückel theory:

$$\log_{10}\gamma_{\pm} = -0.509\sqrt{I}, \tag{4}$$

which is the line drawn through the data in Fig. 2–6.

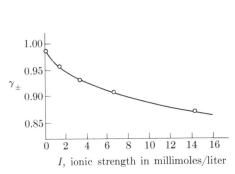

FIG. 2–5. Variation of activity coefficient for silver iodate in potassium nitrate solutions. The circles are the same experimental points as those plotted in Fig. 2–3.

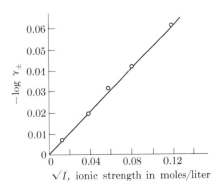

FIG. 2–6.   Fit of experimental activity coefficient values (circles) to the Debye-Hückel limiting law: $-\log \gamma_{\pm} = 0.509\sqrt{I}$.

Theoretical calculation of activity coefficient. In solutions of concentration up to 0.1 molar, it is quite feasible to calculate the values of activity coefficients theoretically. One empirical expression which represents experimental measurements of activity coefficients fairly well is the Davies modification of the Debye-Hückel relation. For an ion of charge z, either positive or negative, the activity coefficient of the ion is given by

$$-\log_{10} \gamma_z = 0.509 \, z^2 \left(\frac{\sqrt{I}}{1 + \sqrt{I}} - 0.2I \right).$$

The constants apply to water solutions at 25°C.

For solutions more concentrated than 0.1 molar, theoretical prediction of activity coefficients is not so successful, especially when mixtures of electrolytes are involved. However, if a high concentration of a single inert electrolyte such as $NaClO_4$ is present, small changes in concentrations of the ions of interest will change the ionic strength of the medium only slightly, and the activity coefficients of the various ions will be essentially constant. This means that the concentration equilibrium constants will be independent of the concentrations of the ions of interest, although they will depend on the concentration of inert electrolyte. The use of a high concentration of inert electrolyte has been successful in unravelling very complicated systems involving complex formation and hydrolysis.

2–5 THE EFFECT OF ACIDITY AND COMPLEXING AGENTS

The number of cases in which the solubility of an ionic salt can be calculated from its solubility product and the known analytical concentration of added salt, as we did in Sections 2–2 and 2–3, is a relatively small fraction of the cases encountered in practice. Even in dilute solutions, other equilibria besides the solubility equilibrium may exist between ions in the solution. This means that the solubility is in general dependent on a number of other equilibrium constants besides the solubility product. Although calculations in these cases are complicated, and are beyond the scope of this little book, the student should be aware that these complications exist.

Acidity. Very common is the reaction of the cation or the anion with water to produce hydroxide complexes or protonated anion species. Equilibria of this type will be discussed in Section 4–3, but we can illustrate the effect of acidity by a simple example. When silver acetate is dissolved in pure water, the principal species in solution are silver ions and acetate

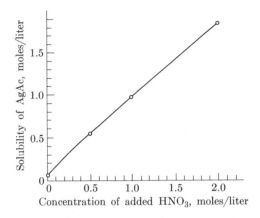

FIG. 2–7.   Solubility of silver acetate in nitric acid. Circles are experimental points. The curve was calculated theoretically.

ions.   We may represent this by the equilibrium

$$AgAc(s) = [Ag^+][Ac^-],$$

where Ac^- stands for the acetate group CH_3COO^-. If nitric acid is added to a saturated solution of silver acetate, the solubility of the salt in the acid is greater than the solubility of the salt in pure water. This is shown by the experimental points in Fig. 2–7.   The line drawn through the points for concentrations below 0.5 molar is the shape that is predicted theoretically.

The explanation for this increase in solubility is very simple.   In the presence of strong acid, a considerable fraction of the acetate groups that dissolve are protonated to form molecular acetic acid.   Thus in addition to the solubility equilibrium, we must consider the dissociation equilibrium of acetic acid:

$$Ac^- + H^+ \rightleftharpoons HAc.$$

The larger the concentration of nitric acid, the more this equilibrium is shifted to the right.   The solubility of the salt is the sum of the concentrations of the acetate groups present, as such, and the concentration of molecular acetic acid, since no other acetate-containing compound has been added to the solution.   Thus, although the mass balance on silver remains

$$[Ag^+] = S,$$

the mass balance on acetate groups becomes

$$[Ac^-] + [HAc] = S,$$

and the methods of calculation used in Sections 2–2 and 2–3 do not apply. A few problems involving equilibria of this type will be found at the end of Chapter 4.

To include the reaction of a cation with water is usually much more difficult, since most metals which form insoluble salts also form very complicated systems of hydroxide complexes. The equilibrium constants for these systems are often very approximate or completely unknown, and calculations on systems where cation hydrolysis occurs are beyond the scope of this book.

However, it is useful to remember qualitatively that anion hydrolysis will be more extensive in acid solutions and cation hydrolysis will be more extensive in basic solutions. Both effects will tend to remove the ions of the salt from solution and hence to increase the solubility of the salt over the value calculated from the solubility product alone.

Complex formation. A related phenomenon is the formation of complexes between the cation and the anion of the salt. An excellent illustration is provided by the experimental results shown in Fig. 2–8 for the solubility of silver chloride in solutions containing excess chloride. Because the solubility data covers a very wide range of variation of the chloride concentration, we have chosen to use a logarithmic scale for the graph. On a log-log plot, the solubility product relation alone predicts a straight line, shown on Fig. 2–8. Clearly this does not represent the experimental results adequately unless the concentration of chloride ion is below

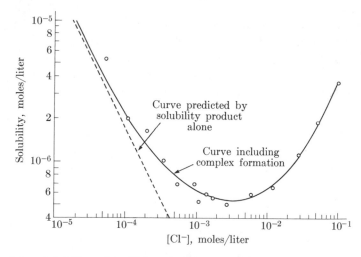

FIG. 2–8. Solubility of AgCl in solutions containing excess chloride. Circles are experimental points. The solid curve was calculated including complex formation. The dotted curve was calculated from the solubility product alone.

10^{-4} mole/liter. In fact, as the concentration of chloride ion is increased, the solubility of silver chloride does not decrease indefinitely, but passes through a minimum and increases again when the chloride ion concentration becomes greater than 10^{-2} mole/liter.

This peculiar behavior is the result of some additional equilibria which exist between silver ions and chloride ions. Besides the solubility equilibrium

$$AgCl(s) \rightleftharpoons Ag^+ + Cl^-,$$

silver ions and chloride ions can combine to form neutral molecules

$$Ag^+ + Cl^- \rightleftharpoons AgCl(aq),$$

where the notation (aq) means that this is a molecule dissolved in aqueous solution and not a solid. As the concentration of chloride ion is increased, more chloride ions combine with the AgCl molecules to give the complex ions $AgCl_2^-$ and $AgCl_3^=$:

$$AgCl(aq) + Cl^- \rightleftharpoons AgCl_2^-,$$
$$AgCl_2^- + Cl^- \rightleftharpoons AgCl_3^=.$$

The total solubility is given by the mass balance on silver. Since all the silver in the solution comes from the dissolved silver chloride, we have

$$S = [Ag^+] + [AgCl] + [AgCl_2^-] + [AgCl_3^=].$$

Because only the first term would be used if we did not realize that the complex ions were present, we see that the actual solubility is greater than that predicted by the solubility product alone. This can also be seen graphically in Fig. 2–8.

Finally, the addition of other salts as precipitating agents, or to adjust the pH of the solution, may cause complexes to form with the ions of interest, and again increase the solubility of the salt to be precipitated.

We may state, as a general conclusion, that in dilute solution, an increase in ionic strength, hydrolysis of the cation or anion, and complex formation all tend to increase the solubility of the salt over that value calculated from the solubility product alone. Thus the methods we have described in this chapter give the minimum possible solubility. Usually, the actual solubility is greater.

PROBLEMS

Use the appendix to obtain the necessary solubility product values for these problems. Starred problems are more difficult than the rest.

Calculate the molar solubility of the following salts in pure water. Convert to gm/liter and compare with typical handbook values.

1. AgCl   2. MgF_2 3. Ag_2SO_4 4. $La(IO_3)_3$

Given the following solubilities, calculate the solubility products.

5. TlCl, $S = 1.4 \times 10^{-2}$ mole/liter

6. SrF_2, $S = 8.5 \times 10^{-4}$ mole/liter

7. $Ce(IO_3)_3$, $S = 1.85 \times 10^{-3}$ mole/liter

8. Mercury(I) exists in solution only as the dimeric ion Hg_2^{++}, so that the solubility product is formulated in terms of this ion. Calculate the solubility of the two salts below in gm/liter.

        (a) Hg_2SO_4, $K_{s0} = [Hg_2^{++}][SO_4^=]$

        (b) Hg_2Cl_2, $K_{s0} = [Hg_2^{++}][Cl^-]^2$

9. All metallic hydroxides except that of magnesium either form complexes in solution or are too soluble to be treated by the simple methods of this section. Calculate the pH of a saturated solution of $Mg(OH)_2$.

What weight of precipitate will be formed (if any) when the following solutions are mixed?

10. 20.0 ml of 5.0×10^{-3} molar KIO_3 and 5.0 ml of 1.0×10^{-2} molar $Pb(NO_3)_2$

11. 1.00 ml of 1.0×10^{-3} molar NaCl and 1.00 ml of 1.0×10^{-3} molar $TlNO_3$

12. 1.00 ml of 0.10 molar NaCl and 10.0 ml of 0.010 molar $AgNO_3$

13. 40.7 mg KF (solid) is shaken with 50 ml 0.0070 molar $CaCl_2$

Calculate the solubility of:

14. $PbSO_4$ in 0.050 molar $Pb(NO_3)_2$

15. $PbSO_4$ in 1.0×10^{-3} molar Na_2SO_4

16. $PbSO_4$ in pure water

17. MgF_2 in 0.10 molar KF

*18. MgF_2 in 1.0×10^{-4} molar $Mg(NO_3)_2$

19. Calculate the fraction of chloride in a 1.0×10^{-3} molar solution of sodium chloride which could be precipitated by adding (a) the stoichiometric amount of $AgNO_3$ of equal concentration; (b) a 10% excess of $AgNO_3$ of equal concentration.

*20. An 0.451 gm sample of AgCl is washed prior to ignition and weighing. Calculate the fraction of the sample which will be lost if it is washed with each of the following solutions.
(a) 200 ml of pure water

(b) 150 ml of 0.10 molar ammonium chloride, followed by 50 ml of pure water

(c) 50 ml of 0.001 molar $AgNO_3$ followed by 150 ml of 0.01 molar HNO_3

Calculate the weight of precipitate formed (if any) when the following solutions are mixed.

21. 25 ml of 0.050 molar $Sr(NO_3)_2$ and 10 ml 0.15 molar Na_2SO_4

22. 1.0 ml of 0.10 molar $AgNO_3$ and 100 ml of 0.0050 molar HCl

23. 0.25 gm KF and 250 ml 0.050 molar $MgCl_2$

*24. Thallium is to be precipitated as the chloride. What volume of 1.00 molar HCl should be added to 10.0 ml of a solution containing 383 mg of thallium in order that precipitation should be 99.5% complete?

*25. Calculate the solubility of $Mg(OH)_2$ in a hydrochloric acid solution whose initial pH is 3.50. What is the pH of the saturated solution?

*26. Consider the general ionic salt M_zX_y. Let its solubility in pure water be S_0. Show that the solubility S in a solution containing Na_zX of analytical concentration C is always less than or equal to S_0 for any positive real value of C provided that the only ions existing in solution are M^{+y}, X^{-z}, Na^+, H^+ and OH^-.

*27. The following data was obtained for the solubility of silver acetate in sodium acetate solutions.

Concentration of NaAc added gm/liter	Solubility of AgAc gm/liter
0.0	11.14
0.93	10.26
4.06	8.14
7.30	6.69
17.3	4.55

Convert this data to moles/liter, and obtain the concentration solubility product of silver acetate.

28. A solution is 0.010 molar in NaCl and 1.0×10^{-3} molar in NaBr. Concentrated silver nitrate solution is added. Does AgCl or AgBr precipitate first? What is the maximum degree of purity which the solution of the second ion can attain?

29. 1.15 gm of $PbSO_4$ is shaken with 100 ml of 0.10 molar KIO_3, and allowed to come to equilibrium. What fraction of the $PbSO_4$ has been converted to solid $Pb(IO_3)_2$?

30. A solution is 0.010 molar in $BaCl_2$ and 0.010 molar in $SrCl_2$. If 100 ml of this solution is mixed with 200 ml of 0.010 molar Na_2SO_4 what fraction of each ion is precipitated?

31. Calculate the solubility of AgCl in 0.050 molar KNO_3, using the Davies equation to estimate activity coefficients.

*32. Apply activity coefficient corrections to the data given in Problem 27 to obtain the thermodynamic (activity) solubility product of silver acetate.

*33. The following data were obtained for the solubility of silver bromate in potassium nitrate solution.

Concentration of KNO_3 added gm/liter	Solubility of $AgBrO_3$ gm/liter
0.0	1.950
4.82	2.238
10.13	2.422
40.54	3.075

(a) Convert the data to moles/liter, plot as in Section 2–4, and extrapolate to zero ionic strength to obtain K_{s0}^0.

(b) From the graph also calculate the mean activity coefficient of silver bromate at an ionic strength of 0.1 mole/liter.

(c) Use this result to calculate the solubility of silver bromate in 0.10 molar $AgNO_3$. What error is introduced if activity coefficients are neglected in this calculation? What effect would the formation of silver bromate complexes, such as $AgBrO_3$ (aq) and $Ag(BrO_3)_2^-$, have on the solubility?

Strong Acids and Bases | 3

"This next bit looks like a little chimney work," he said as he un-
fastened his rope from the anchor piton. This time he wedged his whole
body in the wider part of the crack above where we stood. Sometimes he
could put his back against one side and his knees against the other,
other times he could only wriggle upward an inch at a time, but always
he gave the impression of effortless ease in his movements. I knew by
now that it would take most of my skill and strength to follow his lead.

3-1 THE IONIZATION OF WATER

When water ionizes, a proton (hydrogen ion) is transferred from one
water molecule to another, resulting in a hydrated hydrogen ion and a
hydroxyl ion:

$$H_2O + H_2O \rightleftharpoons H_3O^+ + OH^-.$$

This is, of course, a simplified picture of what actually happens, but it
emphasizes the fact that a hydrogen ion in aqueous solution is *not* a bare
proton, but is very firmly attached to a water molecule. The energy
required to completely dissociate H_3O^+ into H_2O and a proton is about
three times the energy required to break most covalent bonds. H_3O^+ is
further hydrated, with one water molecule attached to each of the hydrogens by hydrogen bonds. These three additional water molecules consti-
tute the *primary hydration shell* of H_3O^+.

These hydrogen bonds (dashed lines) are only about one-tenth as strong as
ordinary covalent bonds, but they are stronger than the hydrogen bonds

31

that join water molecules into aggregates. They remain intact at room temperature, so that the smallest unit in which a hydrated hydrogen ion exists is $H_9O_4^+$. Many more water molecules (secondary hydration shells) are attached by weaker hydrogen bonds, and at the freezing point, the size of these aggregates approaches the size of the ice crystals.

The ion-product of water. For our purposes, however, the number of water molecules attached to an ion in aqueous solution is usually irrelevant, and we shall simplify things by writing all formulas with the least number of water molecules possible unless we wish for some reason to emphasize the fact that an ion is hydrated. The ionization of water is thus abbreviated

$$H_2O \rightleftharpoons H^+ + OH^-,$$

with the understanding that both H^+ and OH^- are hydrated ions. The equilibrium constant for this reaction should be rigorously expressed in terms of activities:

$$\{H^+\}\{OH^-\} = K_a^0\{H_2O\}.$$

Since we shall be dealing with dilute solutions, we can use a simpler expression. In a dilute solution, water is present in large excess, and its concentration, and hence its activity, does not vary appreciably as the concentration of substances dissolved in it varies. Therefore, the concentration of water is usually included in the equilibrium constant.

We define the ion product of water K_w^0 by the relation

$$K_a^0\{H_2O\} = K_w^0 N_{H_2O}$$

where $\{H_2O\}$ is the activity of water expressed in moles/liter, and N_{H_2O} is the mole fraction of water in the solution. In dilute solutions, $\{H_2O\}$ is approximately 55.6 moles/liter, and N_{H_2O} is approximately unity. At 25°C,

$$K_a^0 = 1.80 \times 10^{-16}, \quad \text{and} \quad K_w^0 = 1.00 \times 10^{-14}.$$

If activity coefficients are assumed to be unity, we have the approximate expression:

$$[H^+][OH^-] = K_w = 1.00 \times 10^{-14}. \tag{1}$$

pH of pure water. We need two equations to find the concentrations of hydrogen and hydroxyl ions. The second relation between them is most conveniently provided by a charge balance. In pure water, which is electrically neutral, the total number of positive charges in a given volume must equal the total number of negative charges. The only positive ions

TABLE 3–1

CRITERIA FOR ACID AND BASIC AQUEOUS SOLUTIONS

Acid	Basic
$[H^+] > [OH^-]$ (definition)	$[OH^-] > [H^+]$ (definition)
$[H^+] > 10^{-7}$	$[OH^-] > 10^{-7}$
$[OH^-] < 10^{-7}$	$[H^+] < 10^{-7}$
pH < 7	pH > 7
pOH > 7	pOH < 7

present in pure water are hydrogen ions; the only negative ions are hydroxyl ions. Therefore the concentrations of these must be equal:

$$[H^+] = [OH^-] \tag{2}$$

Alternatively, this relation could be obtained by considering the reaction by which water dissociates. From each molecule of water that ionizes, one hydrogen and one hydroxyl ion is formed.

Substituting from (2) into (1), we have

$$[H^+]^2 = 1.00 \times 10^{-14}, \qquad [H^+] = 1.00 \times 10^{-7},$$

and from (2),

$$[OH^-] = 1.00 \times 10^{-7}.$$

Note that both (1) and (2) are satisfied.

It is common to express these concentrations as logarithmic functions (see Section 1–3). In pure water, at 25°C,

$$pH = -\log[H^+] = 7.00, \qquad pOH = -\log[OH^-] = 7.00.$$

Note that Eq. (1) requires that in all dilute aqueous solutions at 25°C,

$$pH + pOH = 14.00.$$

Pure water is defined to be *neutral* on the acid-base scale of aqueous solutions. If $[H^+]$ is larger than $[OH^-]$, the solution is *acid*, and if $[OH^-]$ is larger than $[H^+]$, the solution is *basic*. Note that if $[H^+]$ is increased over 10^{-7}, $[OH^-]$ is decreased below 10^{-7} in order for the equilibrium relation (1) to be satisfied. These various conditions are summarized in Table 3–1.

Note that the mathematical form of the ion product of water is the same as that of the solubility product of a 1–1 salt such as $AgBrO_3$. For this reason, the mathematical manipulations which we do in this chapter will remind you strongly of those we did in the last chapter. Realizing this similarity, you may find things easier.

3–2 CALCULATION OF pH IN SOLUTIONS OF STRONG ACIDS AND BASES

The extent to which a substance is dissociated to its ions in solution is described by the terms *strong* and *weak*. A strong electrolyte is one which is completely dissociated, and a weak electrolyte is one which is only partly dissociated.*

For purposes of mathematical classification, we shall divide acids and bases into two classes: *strong*, or completely dissociated, and *weak*, or partly dissociated. There is, of course, a continuous gradation from completely dissociated acids like HCl down to almost completely undissociated acids like HCN. A given acid (HIO_3, for example) may be a weak acid in concentrated solutions, but a strong acid in dilute solutions.

Most of the substances listed in Table 3–2 are completely dissociated in solutions more dilute than one mole/liter. Exceptions are iodic acid and strontium, barium, and thallium hydroxides, which are completely dissociated in solutions more dilute than 0.01 mole/liter. Even in very concentrated solutions most of the substances do not exist as covalent molecules, but rather as *ion pairs*, two distinct ions which are nevertheless more strongly associated with each other than would be expected.

Salts formed by the reaction of a strong acid and a strong base (for example, NaCl) are completely dissociated in water and form neutral solutions. Salts formed by the reaction of weak acids and bases are also completely dissociated in water, but their solutions are acid or basic because the ions are themselves acids or bases. This problem is discussed further in the next chapter.

Let us now consider a number of examples of calculating pH in solutions of strong acids and bases.

Example 1. Find the pH of an 0.050 molar solution of HCl. In addition to the ions produced by the dissociation of water, we have introduced H^+ and Cl^- ions by adding hydrochloric acid. The first relation between $[H^+]$ and $[OH^-]$ is the ion product of water

$$[H^+][OH^-] = 1.00 \times 10^{-14}. \tag{1}$$

---

* A slightly different use of the terms *strong* and *weak* is in discussion of the relative strengths of acids or bases. Although both $HClO_4$ and HCl are completely dissociated in water solution, this is merely because water is such a good proton acceptor, a result of the *leveling effect* of the solvent. Pure (glacial) acetic acid is a rather poor proton acceptor, and does not exert this leveling effect. Both $HClO_4$ and HCl are weak electrolytes in glacial acetic acid solutions, but $HClO_4$ is much more dissociated than is HCl. Thus $HClO_4$ is said to be an inherently stronger acid than HCl, even though both are completely dissociated in water.

.

TABLE 3–2

STRONG ACIDS AND BASES

ACIDS	BASES
Completely dissociated in concentration less than 1 mole/liter:	

HCl	LiOH
HBr	NaOH
HI	KOH
$HClO_4$	RbOH
HNO_3	CsOH
H_2SO_4*	
HSCN	

Completely dissociated in concentration less than 0.01 mole/liter:

HIO_3	$Sr(OH)_2$*
	$Ba(OH)_2$*
	TlOH

* These dissociate as follows:

$$H_2SO_4 = H^+ + HSO_4^-, \qquad Sr(OH)_2 = Sr^{++} + 2OH^-.$$

The second relation is called the *proton condition*. One way in which it may be obtained is to consider a mass blance on hydrogen ions. For every hydrogen ion produced by the dissociation of water, one hydroxyl ion is also produced,

$$H_2O \rightleftharpoons H^+ + OH^-,$$

and for every hydrogen ion obtained from the hydrochloric acid, one chloride ion is also obtained,

$$H^+Cl^- \rightleftharpoons H^+ + Cl^-.$$

The concentration of hydrogen ions in the solution is the sum of the concentrations obtained from these two sources:

$$[H^+] = [H^+]_{H_2O} + [H^+]_{HCl},$$
$$[H^+] = [OH^-] + [Cl^-].$$

Note that this relation is identical to the charge balance, since the only positive ions in the solution are hydrogen ions, and the only negative ions are hydroxyl and chloride ions. Finally, we make use of the fact that HCl is completely dissociated, so that

$$[H^+]_{HCl} = [Cl^-] = 0.050.$$

Substituting this in the above equation, we have the final form of the proton condition:

$$[H^+] = [OH^-] + 0.050. \tag{2}$$

It is not necessary to consider the various reactions which produce hydrogen ions in order to obtain the proton condition, but this makes its physical meaning more clear. The proton condition can always be obtained from a charge balance and mass balances on the foreign ions in solutions.

Equations (1) and (2) are simple enough to solve exactly, but it is preferable to make approximations wherever possible, so let us do so. Since the solution is acid, $[OH^-]$ will be less than 10^{-7}, and hence will be quite negligible compared to 0.050 in Eq. (2). The approximate relation is then merely

$$[H^+] = 0.050, \tag{2a}$$

which is just the answer we want. To check whether our approximation was correct, use Eq. (1) to calculate $[OH^-]$:

$$[OH^-] = 2.0 \times 10^{-13},$$

which is certainly negligible compared to 0.050. The pH is calculated as described in Section 1–3:

$$pH = -\log[H^+] = -\log(0.050) = 1.30.$$

All this may seem like shooting squirrels with an elephant gun, but it is important that you thoroughly understand how the mass and charge balances work on simple systems before you apply them to more complicated ones.

Example 2. Find pH and pOH in a 1.0×10^{-3} molar solution of barium hydroxide. As usual we have the ion product of water,

$$[H^+][OH^-] = 1.00 \times 10^{-14}. \tag{1}$$

A charge balance gives

$$[H^+] + 2[Ba^{++}] = [OH^-].$$

Note that Ba^{++} has two charges and hence each ion is counted twice. A mass balance on barium gives

$$[Ba^{++}] = 1.0 \times 10^{-3},$$

which may be substituted in the charge balance to yield the proton condition:

$$[H^+] + 2.0 \times 10^{-3} = [OH^-]. \tag{2}$$

An alternative way of obtaining this expression is by a mass balance on hydroxyl ion: Each molecule of water that dissociates gives one H^+ and one OH^- ion; each mole of $Ba(OH)_2$ gives two moles of OH^-. The sum of these two terms yields $[OH^-]$.

Since there is an excess of hydroxyl ion, the solution will be basic, $[H^+]$ will be less than 10^{-7}, and hence will be negligible in (2) compared to 2.0×10^{-3}. The approximate relation is

$$[OH^-] = 2.0 \times 10^{-3}. \tag{2a}$$

Substitute (2a) into (1) to get $[H^+] = 5.0 \times 10^{-12}$, which is certainly negligible compared to 2.0×10^{-3}. The logarithmic functions are

$$pH = 11.30, \qquad pOH = 2.70.$$

Note that $pH + pOH = 14.00$. This result could have been used to get pH from Eq. (2a) directly.

Example 3. Find the pH of a 1.00×10^{-7} molar solution of HCl. As usual, the ion product of water is

$$[H^+][OH^-] = 1.00 \times 10^{-14}. \tag{1}$$

A mass balance on chloride ion combined with the charge balance gives the proton condition:

$$[H^+] = [OH^-] + 1.00 \times 10^{-7}. \tag{2}$$

Since the solution is so dilute, $[OH^-]$ is *not* negligible compared to 1.00×10^{-7}, and the equations must be solved exactly. Solve (2) for $[OH^-]$ and substitute in (1), to get

$$[H^+]^2 - 1.00 \times 10^{-7}[H^+] - 1.00 \times 10^{-14} = 0.$$

This may be easily solved, using the quadratic formula (Section 1–2), to obtain

$$[H^+] = 1.62 \times 10^{-7},$$
$$pH = 6.79.$$

The negative root of the quadratic is discarded since it is not physically meaningful. To check this result, calculate $[OH^-]$ by means of Eq. (1), obtaining

$$[OH^-] = 6.18 \times 10^{-8},$$

and substitute in Eq. (2) to see that it is satisfied:

$$[H^+] = 0.62 \times 10^{-7} + 1.00 \times 10^{-7} = 1.62 \times 10^{-7},$$

which agrees exactly with the positive root of the quadratic equation.

Example 4. Find the pH of a solution containing 0.020 moles of $Ba(NO_3)_2$ per liter. It may seem obvious to you that this solution will be neutral, but you may be interested to see how this conclusion can be reached using mass and charge balances. A mass balance on barium gives

$$[Ba^{++}] = 0.020, \tag{3}$$

and a mass balance on nitrate, noting that two moles of nitrate are formed for each mole of salt dissolving, gives

$$[NO_3^-] = 0.040. \tag{4}$$

A charge balance on the solution is

$$2[\text{Ba}^{++}] + [\text{H}^+] = [\text{OH}^-] + [\text{NO}_3^-], \tag{5}$$

and when (3) and (4) are substituted in (5), we obtain the proton condition, which is merely

$$[\text{H}^+] = [\text{OH}^-] \tag{2}$$

and is the same as the proton condition for pure water. This may be combined with the ion product of water

$$[\text{H}^+][\text{OH}^-] = 1.00 \times 10^{-14}, \tag{1}$$

to give

$$[\text{H}^+] = 1.00 \times 10^{-7},$$

$$\text{pH} = 7.00,$$

thus proving that the solution is neutral. An alternative approach is to note that there is no external source of hydrogen and hydroxyl ions, and hence the proton condition must be the same as in pure water. Note that the cation of a strong base and the anion of a strong acid are essentially inert, serving only to keep the charges balanced, and do not themselves enter into acid-base reactions at all.

General relation for pH of strong acid. It is instructive to consider the general problem of relating the pH of a strong acid solution to its analytical concentration. In solutions of reasonable concentrations (Example 1), $[\text{H}^+]$ is almost exactly equal to the analytical concentration of the acid. On the other hand, in the limit of pure water, where no acid is present at all, $[\text{H}^+]$ is 10^{-7} mole/liter.

The transition between these two simple limits is given by a general relation which can easily be derived. For a completely dissociated acid of analytical concentration C, the two equations required to define the concentrations $[\text{H}^+]$ and $[\text{OH}^-]$ are the ion product of water:

$$[\text{H}^+][\text{OH}^-] = K_w, \tag{1}$$

and the proton condition,

$$[\text{H}^+] = C + [\text{OH}^-]. \tag{2}$$

Solving (2) for $[\text{OH}^-]$ and substituting in (1) gives

$$[\text{H}^+]([\text{H}^+] - C) = K_w,$$

which is a quadratic function of $[\text{H}^+]$:

$$[\text{H}^+]^2 - C[\text{H}^+] - K_w = 0, \tag{6}$$

but only a linear function of C:

$$C = [H^+] - \frac{K_w}{[H^+]}.\tag{7}$$

In the limit where $[H^+]$ is large compared to $[OH^-]$, the last term of (7) is negligible, giving merely

$$[H^+] = C.\tag{7a}$$

In the opposite limit, where the concentration C is small compared to 10^{-7}, the left-hand side of (7) is negligible, yielding

$$[H^+]^2 = K_w,\tag{7b}$$

or pH $= 7.00$.

If we choose values for C and obtain values for $[H^+]$, as we did in Example 3, plotting Eq. (6) would be very tedious, since a quadratic equation would have to be solved for each value of C. On the other hand, plotting (7) by choosing values for $[H^+]$ and calculating values for C is very simple, and gives the same curve.

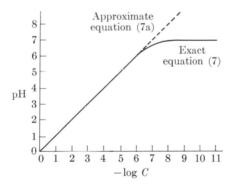

Fig. 3–1. The pH of a strong acid as a function of concentration. Large concentrations are at the left and small concentrations at the right; acid solutions at the bottom, and basic solutions at the top. The solid curve is the exact equation (7). The dotted curve is the approximate equation (7a).

The values of $[H^+]$ normally found in solutions of strong acids range from one mole/liter down to 10^{-7} mole/liter, a factor of ten million in size. The range of C normally covered is even larger. The only practical method of plotting these values is on a logarithmic scale. Because all the numbers are smaller than unity, their logarithms will be negative numbers, and it is convenient to plot the negative logarithms: pH as a function of $-\log C$. These values, obtained from Eq. (7), are plotted in Fig. 3–1.

Note that large values of C give small values of $-\log C$, and small values of C give large values of $-\log C$. This representation of smaller things by larger numbers may seem peculiar at first, but with a little practice (Section 1–3), it is easy to become accustomed to making the mental translation, and the convenience is worth the effort.

Look at Fig. 3–1. Equation (7a),

$$[H^+] = C, \tag{7a}$$

is obeyed until C gets down in the region of 10^{-6} mole/liter. Then $[H^+]$ levels off at 10^{-7} mole/liter, while C becomes as small as you like.

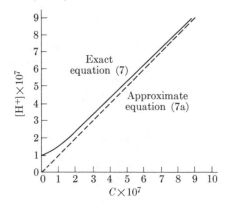

FIG. 3–2. The pH of a strong acid as a function of concentration in very dilute solutions. The solid line is the exact equation (7). The dotted line is the approximate equation (7a). Note that when $C = 0$, pH $= 7.00$.

Figure 3–2 shows the region around 10^{-7} mole/liter plotted on a linear scale. The solid line is the actual concentration $[H^+]$, as given by Eq. (7), and the dashed line is the approximate Eq. (7a). Instead of labeling the coordinate axis of Fig. 3–2 with numbers like $C = 2 \times 10^{-7}$ mole/liter, we have used units of C which are 10^{-7} mole/liter in size, and have labeled the axis $C \times 10^7 = 2$. An alternative way of labeling the axis is to use units of micromoles (10^{-6} mole)/liter, in which case $C = 0.2$ micromole/liter.

PROBLEMS

1. Harned and Hamer measured the ionization constant of water at various temperatures, and found that at 0°C, $K_w = 1.15 \times 10^{-15}$, and at 60°C, $K_w = 9.60 \times 10^{-14}$. Calculate the pH of a neutral solution at each of these temperatures. Why is one of the main controls on a pH meter a temperature compensator?

Calculate pH and pOH in the following solutions at 25°C. Check whether any approximations you make are justified.

2. 0.050 ml of 16 molar nitric acid is mixed with 1 liter of water

3. 0.030 molar potassium hydroxide solution

4. 4.5×10^{-4} molar $Sr(OH)_2$ solution

5. 0.100 mg TlOH in 174 ml water

6. 4.0×10^{-8} molar LiOH solution

7. 1.4×10^{-7} molar $Ba(OH)_2$ solution

8. 15 ml 1.3×10^{-4} molar $Sr (IO_3)_2$ is mixed with 12 ml 0.015 molar HIO_3

9. 150 ml 2.5×10^{-3} molar NaCl is mixed with 100 ml 5.0×10^{-8} molar HCl

*10. Ethanol (C_2H_5OH, abbreviated EtOH) dissociates as follows:

$$EtOH + EtOH \rightleftharpoons EtOH_2^+ + EtO^-.$$

The equilibrium constant for this reaction at 25°C is

$$[EtOH_2^+][EtO^-] = 8 \times 10^{-20}.$$

Calculate the concentrations of each of the two ions in pure ethanol. What criteria analogous to Table 3–1 exist for acid and basic solutions in ethanol?

*11. Calculate the concentrations of the various ions in an 0.010 molar solution of sodium ethoxide ($Na^+ OEt^-$) in ethanol.

*12. Derive a relation between pH and the analytical concentration C of a strong base. To what equations does this reduce when the solution is fairly concentrated or very dilute? Plot pH as a function of $-\log C$ and compare with Figs. 3–1 and 3–2.

*13. In this chapter, we have used the approximation that activity coefficients are unity. Rigorously, we should use the definition $pH = -\log [H^+]\gamma_{H^+}$, and the equilibrium expression

$$[H^+][OH^-]\gamma_{H^+}\gamma_{OH^-} = K_w^0 N_{H_2O},$$

where N_{H_2O} is the fraction of the total number of moles present which is water. A much less stringent approximation, however, is that the activity coefficients of all univalent ions are the same function of the ionic strength ($\gamma_H^+ = \gamma_{OH}^-$). Show that under this approximation, the addition of the salt of a strong acid and a strong base to pure water does not affect the pH by more than 0.01 units until the concentration of salt reaches 1 mole/liter.

*14. The mean activity coefficient of hydrochloric acid in an 0.500 molar aqueous solution is 0.757. Calculate the pH of 0.500 molar HCl. Compare with the value calculated neglecting activity coefficients.

Weak Acids and Bases | 4

"I think we're over the chimneys and cracks," he said as I clambered over the edge of the ledge and sat panting by his side. "If you look over there to the right, you will see that it is a bit broken up, and not quite vertical. I think we can pick our way up that face with a little luck."

I had my doubts, but I held his rope while he inched out on the wall. His feet never dangled free, but there were times that I thought he must be standing on the discolorations in the rock. Hold by hold be moved upwards, never seeming to notice the five hundred feet of space below him.

4–1 pH OF A WEAK ACID

Most acids in aqueous solution are incompletely dissociated at the usual concentrations. These are called weak acids, in contrast to strong acids (Table 3–2), which are completely dissociated. An acid which can lose only one hydrogen ion is called a *monoprotic** acid, and its dissociation can be represented by the familiar equilibrium

$$HA \rightleftharpoons H^+ + A^-.$$

The equilibrium constant expression is rigorously

$$\{H^+\}\{A^-\} = K_a\{HA\},$$

but we shall assume that activities are equal to concentrations, and use the approximate expression

$$[H^+][A^-] = K_a[HA].$$

We have already met briefly with the weak monoprotic acid problem when we discussed the solution of simultaneous equations (Example 1, Section 1–1). In this chapter we shall investigate more thoroughly this important type of equilibrium.

---

* It is also called *monobasic*, indicating that one mole reacts with one equivalent of base.

The ionization constant K_a for a weak acid can vary over a very wide range of values. The ionization constants for a number of common acids are given in the appendix. In aqueous solutions, acids with K_a greater than 1.0 are essentially completely dissociated at concentrations less than 0.1 molar, and can be considered to be strong acids. A borderline case is iodic acid, with $K_a = 0.16$, which is also listed in Table 3–2 with the strong acids. Acids with K_a smaller than 10^{-14} are negligibly dissociated at all concentrations in aqueous solutions, because the ionization of water produces as much or more hydrogen ion than the ionization of the acid. The pH of solutions of such acids varies only slightly from 7.00.

Example 1. Find the concentrations of all species in a 0.010 molar solution of acetic acid, with $K_a = 1.75 \times 10^{-5}$. We have the equilibria

$$[H^+][Ac^-] = 1.75 \times 10^{-5}[HAc], \tag{1}$$

$$[H^+][OH^-] = 1.00 \times 10^{-14}. \tag{2}$$

The charge balance gives the proton condition directly:

$$[H^+] = [Ac^-] + [OH^-]. \tag{3}$$

Since the analytical concentration of the acid is 0.010 mole/liter, and all the acid put in the solution must exist either as HAc or Ac^-, the mass balance on acetate is

$$[HAc] + [Ac^-] = 0.010. \tag{4}$$

These four equations in four unknowns must be solved simultaneously to give the answer to the problem.

Let us simplify the problem by making two approximations. Since the solution is acid, assume that $[OH^-]$ is negligible compared to $[Ac^-]$ in Eq. (3):

$$[H^+] = [Ac^-]. \tag{3a}$$

Furthermore, let us guess (we might not be right) that the acid is only slightly dissociated, and that $[Ac^-]$ is negligible compared to $[HAc]$ in Eq. (4):

$$[HAc] = 0.010. \tag{4a}$$

With these approximations, the problem becomes much simpler. Of course, they might not be correct, and if they are not, the answers we obtain by solving the four approximate Eqs. (1), (2), (3a), and (4a), will not satisfy the exact Eqs. (1), (2), (3), and (4). Let us hope they are correct.

Substituting (3a) and (4a) in (1) gives

$$[H^+]^2 = (1.75 \times 10^{-5})(1.0 \times 10^{-2}),$$

$$[H^+] = 4.18 \times 10^{-4},$$

$$pH = 3.38.$$

From (2), $[OH^-] = 2.39 \times 10^{-11}$.

From (3),

$$[Ac^-] = 4.18 \times 10^{-4}.$$

Substituting these values in (4) to check, we find that it is satisfied to within 4%:

$$[HAc] + [Ac^-] = 4.18 \times 10^{-4} + 1.00 \times 10^{-2} = 1.04 \times 10^{-2}.$$

The other exact equations are satisfied to within the rounding-off errors since we used them to calculate the answers. So long as we do not need a more exact answer than ±4%, the approximate answer we have obtained here is satisfactory. If we need a more exact answer, we would have to abandon the approximation (4a) and use the exact equation (4). This would involve solving a quadratic equation, but would still be feasible. The approximation (3a) is extremely good, since $[OH^-]$ is only one ten-millionth of $[Ac^-]$, and hence is quite negligible.

Example 2. Find the concentrations of all species in a 1.00×10^{-3} molar solution of HF, which has $K_a = 6.75 \times 10^{-4}$. We have the two equilibria as before:

$$[H^+][F^-] = 6.75 \times 10^{-4}[HF], \tag{1}$$

$$[H^+][OH^-] = 1.00 \times 10^{-14}, \tag{2}$$

and the charge and mass balances:

$$[H^+] = [F^-] + [OH^-], \tag{3}$$

$$[HF] + [F^-] = 1.00 \times 10^{-3}. \tag{4}$$

Making the same approximations as in Example 1, we obtain:

$$[H^+] = [F^-], \tag{3a}$$

$$[HF] = 1.00 \times 10^{-3}; \tag{4a}$$

Substituting (3a) and (4a) in (1), we have

$$[H^+]^2 = (6.75 \times 10^{-4})(1.00 \times 10^{-3}),$$

$$[H^+] = 8.2 \times 10^{-4}.$$

From (2),

$$[OH^-] = 1.22 \times 10^{-11}.$$

From (3),

$$[F^-] = 8.2 \times 10^{-4}.$$

Substituting these results in the exact mass balance (4) to check gives

$$[F^-] + [HF] = 8.2 \times 10^{-4} + 10.0 \times 10^{-4} = 1.82 \times 10^{-3},$$

which is in error by almost a factor of two. One of our approximations must have been incorrect.

Certainly $[OH^-]$ is negligible compared to $[F^-]$ in (3), and hence it follows that the first approximation (Eq. 3a) is still good. The second approximation (Eq. 4a) must be discarded. The opposite approximation, complete dissociation, gives

$$[H^+] = [F^-] = 1.00 \times 10^{-3},$$

and from (1),

$$[HF] = 1.48 \times 10^{-3}.$$

Checking in (4), we obtain

$$[F^-] + [HF] = 2.48 \times 10^{-3},$$

which is again in error by more than a factor of two. Thus neither slight dissociation nor complete dissociation is a good approximation in this problem, and the exact equation (4) must be used. Note that (3a) is still valid, even though (4a) is not.

Substituting (3a) and (4) in (1) yields

$$[H^+]^2 = (6.75 \times 10^{-4})(1.00 \times 10^{-3} - [H^+]),$$

a quadratic which can be solved by the formula of Section 1–2 to give

$$[H^+] = 5.5 \times 10^{-4}, \qquad pH = 3.26.$$

From (2) $[OH^-] = 1.8 \times 10^{-11}.$

From (3) $[F^-] = 5.5 \times 10^{-4}.$

From (1) $[HF] = 4.48 \times 10^{-4}.$

And checking in the original exact equations (1), (2), (3), and (4), we find that they are all satisfied to within the rounding-off errors.

We went through two seemingly reasonable. approximations in this example only to find that neither of them produced answers that satisfied the exact equations. As a result, we had to solve the equations without using any approximations on the mass balance (Eq. 4), although the neglect of $[OH^-]$ in the charge balance (Eq. 3) was a good approximation.*

---

* In concentrated HF solutions, the ion HF_2^- becomes important, but in these dilute solutions, its concentration is negligible. From the equilibrium relation

$$[HF_2^-] = 3.9[F^-][HF],$$

we calculate for this example that

$$[HF_2^-] = 9.6 \times 10^{-7},$$

which is less than 0.1% of the analytical concentration of HF. Calculations involving complexes such as this are beyond the scope of this book in most cases.

The following generalizations about approximations may be useful to you in solving weak acid problems:

1. *If C is small compared to* 10^{-7}, both [HA] and [A$^-$] are negligible compared to [H$^+$] and [OH$^-$], and the pH will be 7, independent of concentration.

2. *If C is large compared to* 10^{-7}, [OH$^-$] is usually negligible compared to [H$^+$].

3. *If C is small compared to* K_a, [HA] is usually negligible compared to [A$^-$].

4. *If C is large compared to* K_a, [A$^-$] is often negligible compared to [HA]. Do not use these generalizations blindly, however, since they do not always hold. Always check your answers in the exact equations to make sure they are correct.

General relation between pH and concentration. Since we are now familiar with the problem of the weak monoprotic acid, let us examine the general relation between the pH of a solution of the acid HA and its analytical concentration C. There are four concentrations to be considered, [H$^+$], [A$^-$], [HA], and [OH$^-$], and there are four relations among them. We shall assume that K_a, K_w, and C are known. The acid ionization equilibrium gives

$$[H^+][A^-] = K_a[HA]. \tag{1}$$

The ion product of water gives

$$[H^+][OH^-] = K_w. \tag{2}$$

A charge balance gives the proton condition:

$$[H^+] = [A^-] + [OH^-]. \tag{3}$$

A mass balance on the anion A gives

$$[HA] + [A^-] = C, \tag{4}$$

indicating that all the acid put in solution either remains un-ionized or produces anions.

At this point the most straightforward approach is to systematically eliminate the unknowns to obtain a relation for [H$^+$] in terms of C, K_a, and K_w, using the rules outlined in Section 1–1. [HA] and [OH$^-$] each appear in two equations; [H$^+$] and [A$^-$] each appear in three equations. Let us eliminate [HA] first. Solve Eq. (4) for [HA], substitute it in Eq. (1), and solve the resulting equation for [A$^-$]:

$$[A^-] = \frac{CK_a}{K_a + [H^+]}.$$

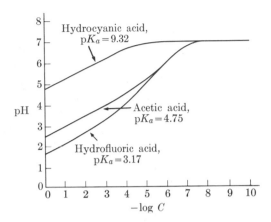

FIG. 4–1. Variation of the pH of several weak acids with concentration. In sufficiently dilute solution, at the right-hand side of the diagram, pH = 7.00 for all weak acids.

Next solve (2) for $[OH^-]$, and substitute both in (3):

$$[H^+] = \frac{CK_a}{K_a + [H^+]} + \frac{K_w}{[H^+]}. \tag{5}$$

This function is most easily plotted if values are assumed for $[H^+]$ and C is calculated. Solving (5) for C, we have

$$C = \left(1 + \frac{[H^+]}{K_a}\right)\left([H^+] - \frac{K_w}{[H^+]}\right). \tag{5}$$

Figure 4–1 is a plot of pH as a function of $-\log C$ for three common acids, hydrofluoric, acetic, and hydrocyanic.

Note first of all that at sufficiently small concentrations (large values of $-\log C$), the pH is 7.00 independent of C, because the hydrogen ions come principally from the dissociation of water, not the acid. At higher concentrations, the acid dissociation contributes hydrogen ions and pH decreases. If the acid were completely dissociated, the curve of Fig. 3–1 would be obtained, but because the dissociation is less in more concentrated solutions, the pH does not change so rapidly with concentration.

Hydrocyanic acid, having a very small ionization constant, ceases to contribute appreciable hydrogen ions when its concentration falls below about 10^{-5} molar. Acetic acid, and hydrofluoric acid, having larger ionization constants, contribute more hydrogen ions at any given concentration, and do not cease contributing until their concentrations fall below 10^{-8} mole/liter.

Logarithmic concentration diagrams. The remainder of this section is concerned with a very interesting and useful graphical representation of the weak acid equilibrium. The logarithmic concentration diagram displays graphically the equilibria and mass balances for given values of K_a and C. The final relation, the proton condition, can often be applied to the diagram by merely finding the correct intersection of two lines, and many problems can thus be solved without any numerical calculations.

The concentrations of the various species in solution can be expressed as simple functions of the pH by combining Eqs. (1), (2), and (4) with the definition of pH. By definition, we have

$$\log [\text{H}^+] = -\text{pH}.$$

Combining this with the ion product of water [Eq. (2)], we have

$$\log [\text{OH}^-] = \text{pH} - \text{p}K_w.$$

In Fig. 4–2, the two straight lines of slope -1 and $+1$ give the logarithms of the concentrations of H^+ and OH^- as functions of pH.

By eliminating [HA] between Eqs. (1) and (4) as before, we obtain a relation for [A$^-$] in terms of [H$^+$] and the known values of C and K_a:

$$[\text{A}^-] = \frac{CK_a}{K_a + [\text{H}^+]}. \tag{6}$$

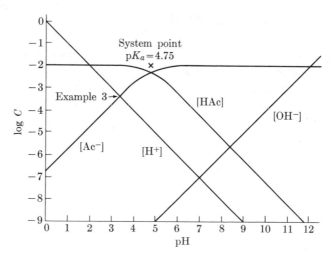

Fig. 4–2. Logarithmic concentration diagram for 1.0×10^{-2} molar acetic acid.

Similarly, by eliminating $[A^-]$ between (1) and (4), we obtain a relation for $[HA]$ in terms of $[H^+]$ and the known values of C and K_a:

$$[HA] = \frac{C[H^+]}{K_a + [H^+]}. \tag{7}$$

These two functions are plotted in Fig. 4–2 for 0.01 molar acetic acid ($C = 10^{-2}$, $pK_a = 4.75$). On the left side of the diagram, where $[H^+]$ is much larger than K_a, we see that $\log [HA]$ is independent of pH and $\log [A^-]$ varies linearly with pH. This can be seen algebraically if K_a is neglected compared to $[H^+]$ in the denominators of Eqs. (6) and (7):

$$\log [A^-] = \log C - pK_a + pH, \tag{6a}$$

$$\log [IIA] = \log C. \tag{7a}$$

On the right-hand side of the diagram, where $[H^+]$ is much smaller than K_a, we see that $\log [A^-]$ is independent of pH and $\log [HA]$ varies linearly with pH. This can be seen algebraically if $[H^+]$ is neglected compared to K_a in the denominators of (6) and (7):

$$\log [\Lambda^-] = \log C, \tag{6b}$$

$$\log [HA] = \log C + pK_a - pH. \tag{7b}$$

If these limiting straight lines are drawn, they all intersect at the point where $pH = pK_a$ on the horizontal axis and at $\log C$ on the vertical axis. This point is called the *system point*.

In the region about one pH unit on either side of the system point, the lines for $\log [A^-]$ and $\log [HA]$ are curved; the curves are given by Eqs. (6) and (7). Note that when $pH = pK_a$,

$$[A^-] = [HA] = \tfrac{1}{2}C,$$

so that the curves cross at a point 0.30 logarithmic units below the system point.

With this introduction, it is now possible to formulate a set of rules for constructing a logarithmic-concentration diagram which avoid numerical calculations entirely. For accurate results, it is best to use graph paper divided into millimeter squares.

1. *Mark the scales* on the graph as in Fig. 4–2, making each logarithmic unit 20 mm or 2 large divisions. For problems dealing with very dilute solutions, it may be desirable to make the concentration scale cover a different range, and for problems involving basic solutions, it may be desirable to shift the pH scale so it covers the range from 2 to 14 instead of from 0 to 12.

2. *Locate the system point* at pH $= pK_a$ on the horizontal scale and at a concentration equal to the analytical concentration C of the acid on the vertical scale.

3. *Draw a horizontal line* through the system point, leaving out the section one pH unit on either side of the system point.

4. *Draw lines of slope* $+1$ *and* -1 downward through the system point, leaving out the sections one pH unit on either side of the system point. A 45-degree triangle is useful for this operation.

5. *Complete the curves.* Now join the horizontal line on one side of the system point with the sloping line on the other side of the system point by a short curve, making sure the curve passes through the point 0.3 logarithmic units (6 mm) below the system point. The two curves should cross at that point. A small French curve or a cardboard template is useful for this operation. The exact shape of the curved sections is not too critical, but if a cardboard template is made, it should fit a curve calculated from Eqs. (6) and (7).

6. *Label the curves.* The curve whose horizontal section lies to the left is labeled [HA] and gives the concentration of undissociated acid as a function of pH. The curve whose horizontal section lies to the right is labeled [A$^-$] and gives the concentration of anion as a function of pH.

7. *Finally draw the* [H$^+$] *and* [OH$^-$] *lines.* These two lines cross at pH $= 7$ at a logarithmic concentration of -7, and have slopes of -1 and $+1$, respectively. They are most easily drawn using a 45-degree triangle.

Note that changing the concentration of the solution shifts the [HA] and [A$^-$] curves up and down, changing the ionization constant of the acid shifts the [HA] and [A$^-$] curves right and left, but neither operation affects the position of the [H$^+$] and [OH$^-$] lines. If you are ambitious, you might trace the [HA] and [A$^-$] curves on a transparent sheet, and place them over the fixed [H$^+$] and [OH$^-$] curves in various positions for the various problems that we do.

Let us consider some examples which demonstrate how the diagram is used in actual calculations.

Example 3. Find graphically the pH of 1.0×10^{-2} molar acetic acid. This problem, solved numerically in Example 1, can also be solved graphically, using Fig. 4–2. The diagram contains all the information in the two equilibrium relations (1) and (2) and the mass balance (4). If we apply the proton condition (3) to the diagram, we will have solved the problem. The proton condition is

$$[H^+] = [Ac^-] + [OH^-]. \tag{3}$$

Follow the [H$^+$] line down until it meets the first line of slope $+1$, which is [Ac$^-$]. At this point [OH$^-$] is less than 10^{-9}, which is surely negligible, and the pH of the solution is given by the condition

$$[H^+] = [Ac^-],$$

that is, by the intersection of the $[H^+]$ and the $[Ac^-]$ curves.

We quickly obtain the other concentrations from the graph by merely reading the value of $\log C$ corresponding to this pH:

$$\text{pH} = 3.37 \quad \text{(from intersection)};$$

$$\log [H^+] = -3.37, \quad [H^+] = 4.26 \times 10^{-4},$$

$$\log [Ac^-] = -3.37, \quad [Ac^-] = 4.26 \times 10^{-4},$$

$$\log [HAc] = -2.00, \quad [HAc] = 1.00 \times 10^{-2},$$

$$\log [OH^-] < -9, \quad [OH^-] < 10^{-9}.$$

These answers are approximately correct, as can be seen by substituting them in the exact equations, which are satisfied to within the errors in reading the graph.

Example 4. Find graphically the pH of 10^{-3} molar HF. This problem, solved numerically in Example 2, can be solved graphically by means of a logarithmic concentration diagram, Fig. 4–3. Equations (1), (2), and (4) are embodied in the diagram, and Eq. (3),

$$[H^+] = [F^-] + [OH^-], \tag{3}$$

must be satisfied. Following the $[H^+]$ line down, we see that it meets $[F^-]$ while $[OH^-]$ is still very small, and so the intersection of the $[H^+]$ and $[F^-]$ curves

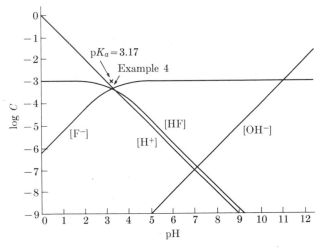

FIG. 4–3.   Logarithmic concentration diagram for 1.0×10^{-3} molar HF.

satisfies the proton condition (3). This intersection gives

$$pH = 3.25, \qquad [H^+] = 5.6 \times 10^{-4},$$

$$\log [F^-] = -3.25, \qquad [F^-] = 5.6 \times 10^{-4},$$

$$\log [HF] = -3.34, \qquad [HF] = 4.5 \times 10^{-4},$$

which agree, to within 5%, with the results obtained numerically. Depending on how accurately the curved section of the $[F^-]$ curve is drawn, the error may be larger or smaller.

Example 5. Find the concentrations of all species in a 1.00×10^{-4} molar solution of HCN, whose dissociation constant is 4.8×10^{-10}. The equations to be solved are

$$[H^+][CN^-] = 4.8 \times 10^{-10}[HCN], \tag{1}$$

$$[H^+][OH^-] = 1.00 \times 10^{-14}, \tag{2}$$

$$[H^+] = [CN^-] + [OH^-], \tag{3}$$

$$[CN^-] + [HCN] = 1.00 \times 10^{-4}. \tag{4}$$

We can make a graphical solution, using a logarithmic concentration diagram (Fig. 4–4), although it is not so accurate as in Examples 3 and 4. Equations (1), (2), and (4) are embodied in the diagram, and Eq. (3) must be satisfied. Following the $[H^+]$ line down, it intersects the $[CN^-]$ line first, at the point where

$$pH = 6.65, \qquad [H^+] = 2.24 \times 10^{-7},$$

$$\log [CN^-] = -6.65, \qquad [CN^-] = 2.24 \times 10^{-7},$$

$$\log [HCN] = -4.00, \qquad [HCN] = 1.00 \times 10^{-4},$$

$$\log [OH^-] = -7.35, \qquad [OH^-] = 4.46 \times 10^{-8}.$$

Let us compare these results with a numerical solution. Neglecting $[CN^-]$, which is about 10^{-7}, compared to $[HCN]$, which is about 10^{-4}, in (4), and substituting in (1), we have

$$[H^+][CN^-] = 4.8 \times 10^{-14}. \tag{1a}$$

Substituting for $[CN^-]$ from (1a) and for $[OH^-]$ from (2) in (3), we have

$$[H^+] = \frac{4.8 \times 10^{-14}}{[H^+]} + \frac{1.00 \times 10^{-14}}{[H^+]},$$

$$[H^+]^2 = 5.8 \times 10^{-14}, \qquad [H^+] = 2.4 \times 10^{-7}.$$

From (1a), $\qquad\qquad\qquad [CN^-] = 2.0 \times 10^{-7}.$

From (2), $\qquad\qquad\qquad [OH^-] = 4.2 \times 10^{-8},$

and from (4), $\qquad\qquad\qquad [HCN] = 1.00 \times 10^{-4}.$

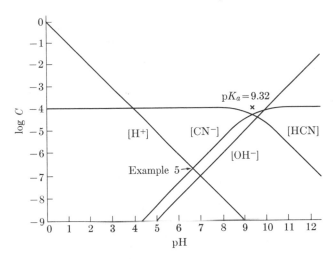

F$_{IG}$. 4–4.   Logarithmic concentration diagram for 1.0×10^{-4} molar HCN.

Substituting back in the original equations, we can easily verify that all are satisfied to within the rounding-off errors. In this case, the approximation of slight dissociation ([HCN] large compared to [CN$^-$]) was good, but the approximation of neglecting [OH$^-$] was not.

The answers obtained graphically disagree somewhat with the answers obtained numerically because [OH$^-$] is not completely negligible compared to [CN$^-$] in (3). However, the error is only about 10% in [H$^+$], which may be satisfactory for many purposes.

The largest error that can be introduced from this source by the graphical method occurs when the [A$^-$] and [OH$^-$] lines coincide. At this point, [H$^+$] is twice the value obtained from the intersection, and the pH obtained graphically is 0.30 unit too small. When the [OH$^-$] line is met first (for example, in 10^{-6} molar HCN), the answer obtained is always pH = 7.00. In the case where the [A$^-$] and [OH$^-$] lines are close together, the graphical solution can give a good idea of the relative values of concentrations, the exact answer being obtained numerically.

4–2 pH OF A WEAK BASE

Soluble weak bases which combine with only one proton are treated by exactly the same mathematical formalism as was used for weak monoprotic acids. For example, when ammonia is dissolved in water, it abstracts a proton from a water molecule, giving an ammonium ion and a hydroxyl ion:

$$NH_3 + H_2O \rightleftharpoons NH_4^+ + OH^-.$$

In earlier books aqueous ammonia was usually written NH_4OH instead of

NH_3 in order to emphasize the fact that it gave NH_4^+ ions on dissociation. There has been considerable controversy during the past few years over the best way of representing aqueous ammonia, and even now all the details have not been cleared up.

The most revealing studies have been those in which the rate of isotope exchange on ammonium ion is followed by nuclear magnetic resonance spectroscopy. The best evidence available at present indicates that no such *molecule* as NH_4OH exists, but rather that the dissolved ammonia molecule is hydrogen-bonded to at least three water molecules:

$$
\begin{array}{ccccc}
H & & H & & H \\
| & & | & & | \\
H-N---H-O----H-O---* \\
| & & | & & \vdots \\
H & & H & & * \\
& & | & & \\
& & H-O---* \\
& & & \vdots \\
& & & * \\
\end{array}
$$

The hydrogen bonds, indicated by dashed lines, are about one-twentieth as strong as a normal covalent bond, such as the N-H bond of NH_3. A true NH_4OH molecule would have the ammonia bonded to a single water molecule by a normal covalent bond, but no evidence has been found for such a molecule.

The addition of a hydrogen ion (from an acid or from another water molecule) at any one of the starred positions causes the proton nearest to the nitrogen atom to move the short distance along the hydrogen bond. The result is the formation of an ammonium ion. For example, if a proton is added to the extreme right-hand side of the above structure, we end up with:

$$
\begin{array}{ccccc}
H & & H & & H \\
|+ & & | & & | \\
H-N-H---O-H----O-H \\
| & & | & & \\
H & & H & & \\
& & | & & \\
& & H-O \\
\end{array}
$$

Because of the complicated nature of the ionization of ammonia, we have chosen to represent aqueous ammonia by the formula NH_3, with the understanding that a number of water molecules are loosely attached, and participate intimately in the ionization process.*

---

* Writing NH_4OH instead of NH_3 for ammonia is analogous to writing H_3OOH instead of H_2O for water.

The same is true of organic amines. For example, pyridine shows a weakly basic reaction in water. We represent the ionization as follows:

$$\text{(pyridine)} \quad N + H_2O \rightleftharpoons \text{(pyridine)} NH^+ + OH^-.$$

A number of ammonia derivatives which are monoprotic bases are listed in the Appendix. Metal hydroxides are either nearly completely dissociated (Section 3–2) or they form complex ions with several hydroxyl groups, so they are considered to be beyond the scope of this book.

The ionization of a weak base may be generalized to be

$$B + H_2O \rightleftharpoons BH^+ + OH^-.$$

Since, in dilute solution, the activity of water is nearly constant, and the activities of the other species are approximately equal to their concentrations, we shall use the approximate equilibrium expression

$$[BH^+][OH^-] = K_b[B]. \tag{1}$$

The ion product of water

$$[H^+][OH^-] = K_w, \tag{2}$$

a charge balance (the proton condition),

$$[H^+] + [BH^+] = [OH^-], \tag{3}$$

and a mass balance,

$$[BH^+] + [B] = C, \tag{4}$$

provide the four equations necessary to relate the four concentrations [B], [BH^+], [H^+], and [OH^-] to the known analytical concentration C and ionization constants K_b and K_w.

Example 6. Find the concentrations of all species in an 0.010 molar solution of ammonia, $K_b = 1.78 \times 10^{-5}$. We have the four equations

$$[NH_4^+][OH^-] = 1.78 \times 10^{-5}[NH_3], \tag{1}$$

$$[H^+][OH^-] = 1.00 \times 10^{-14}, \tag{2}$$

$$[H^+] + [NH_4^+] = [OH^-], \tag{3}$$

$$[NH_4^+] + [NH_3] = 0.010. \tag{4}$$

Since the solution is basic, we can neglect [H^+] compared to [OH^-] in (3):

$$[NH_4^+] = [OH^-]. \tag{3a}$$

A possible approximation on (4) is to neglect [NH_4^+] compared to [NH_3]:

$$[NH_3] = 0.010. \tag{4a}$$

TABLE 4–1

ANALOGY BETWEEN WEAK ACID AND WEAK BASE EQUATIONS

Weak acid	Weak base
(1) $[H^+][A^-] = K_a[HA]$	(1) $[OH^-][BH^+] = K_b[B]$
(2) $[H^+][OH^-] = K_w$	(2) $[OH^-][H^+] = K_w$
(3) $[H^+] = [OH^-] + [A^-]$	(3) $[OH^-] = [H^+] + [BH^+]$
(4) $[HA] + [A^-] = C$	(4) $[B] + [BH^+] = C$

$[H^+]$	replaced by	$[OH^-]$
$[OH^-]$	replaced by	$[H^+]$
$[HA]$	replaced by	$[B]$
$[A^-]$	replaced by	$[BH^+]$
K_a	replaced by	K_b

Substituting (3a) and (4a) in (1) gives

$$[OH^-]^2 = (1.78 \times 10^{-5})(1.0 \times 10^{-2}),$$

$$[OH^-] = 4.22 \times 10^{-4}.$$

From (2), $\qquad [H^+] = 2.37 \times 10^{-11}.$

From (3), $\qquad [NH_4^+] = 4.22 \times 10^{-4}.$

Checking by substituting in the exact equations, we see they are satisfied to within 4%.

Example 6 is exactly the same formally as Example 1. The only difference is that HAc, Ac^-, H^+, and OH^- have been replaced by NH_3, NH_4^+, OH^-, and H^+, respectively. This formal analogy can be clearly seen by comparing the equations governing the equilibrium in the two cases. Analogous equations have been given the same numbers, and the two problems compared, in Table 4–1.

Since the mathematical equations are of the same form, their solutions will be also of the same form. The exact solution of the weak base problem is analogous to Eq. (5) of Section 4–1, and a plot analogous to Fig. 4–1 can be made for a weak base. (See Problem 18.)

A logarithmic concentration diagram for 10^{-2} molar ammonia (Fig. 4–5) can be constructed by analogy with the weak-acid diagram (Fig. 4–2). The system point is where $pOH = pK_b$, and in terms of pH this is

$$pH = pK_w - pK_b.$$

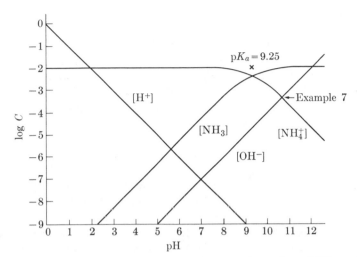

Fig. 4–5. Logarithmic concentration diagram for 1.0×10^{-2} molar ammonia.

For ammonia,

$$pK_b = 4.75, \qquad pH = 14.00 - 4.75 = 9.25.$$

For a concentration of 10^{-2} mole/liter, the system point is placed as shown in Fig. 4–5. The curve for $[NH_4^+]$ is horizontal to the left of the system point and has slope -1 to the right; the curve for $[NH_3]$ has slope $+1$ to the left of the system point and is horizontal to the right. The curves for $[H^+]$ and $[OH^-]$ are the same as before—straight lines of slope -1 and $+1$, respectively.

Example 7. Find graphically the pH of 0.010 molar ammonia. Figure 4–5 can be used for the calculation done numerically in Example 6, since Eqs. (1), (2), and (4) are embodied in the diagram. Equation (3) will fix a point which gives the solution:

$$[OH^-] = [NH_4^+] + [H^+]. \qquad (3)$$

Following the $[OH^-]$ line down, we see that it meets the $[NH_4^+]$ line at a point where $[H^+]$ is still quite negligible. The intersection of $[OH^-]$ and $[NH_4^+]$ thus gives the answer. At this point,

$$pH = 10.62, \qquad [H^+] = 2.4 \times 10^{-11},$$
$$\log [NH_4^+] = -3.38, \qquad [NH_4^+] = 4.2 \times 10^{-4},$$
$$\log [OH^-] = -3.38, \qquad [OH^-] = 4.2 \times 10^{-4},$$
$$\log [NH_3] = -2.00, \qquad [NH_3] = 1.0 \times 10^{-2},$$

which are the same as the results obtained numerically in Example 6.

4–3 GENERALIZED ACIDS AND BASES

The salt of a strong base and a weak acid, such as sodium cyanide, produces a basic solution when dissolved in water. The term usually applied to this phenomenon is *hydrolysis,** but the equilibrium involved is the same as for the dissociation of the weak acid. When the salt is dissolved in water, the anion extracts a proton from the water, giving the weak acid and a hydroxyl ion:

$$A^- + H_2O \rightleftharpoons HA + OH^-.$$

The anion of the weak acid, in the reaction above, behaves like ammonia or pyridine in removing a proton from the water. In other words, A^- is a weak base, differing from the usual weak bases only in its charge.

This leads us to the *Bronsted-Lowry* definition of acids and bases: An acid is a *proton donor* and a base is a *proton acceptor*. Removal of a proton from any acid produces its *conjugate base*. In the case above, the anion A^- is the base conjugate to the weak acid HA. Water is the base conjugate to the acid H_3O^+. Hydroxyl ion is the base conjugate to the acid water. Ammonia is the base conjugate to the acid NH_4^+.

In the ionization of a weak acid, a proton is transferred from the acid HA to the base H_2O. In the ionization of water, one water molecule acts as an acid (proton donor) and one as a base (proton acceptor). A substance which can act as either an acid or a base is *amphiprotic*, or an *ampholyte*. We shall encounter ampholytes again in our discussion of polyprotic acids in Section 4–5.

The basic ionization constant (or hydrolysis constant) of A^- bears a simple relation to the acid ionization constant of HA. Let us define

$$K_b^{A^-} = \frac{[HA][OH^-]}{[A^-]} \quad \text{and} \quad K_a^{HA} = \frac{[H^+][A^-]}{[HA]}.$$

Multiplying the two equations together gives

$$K_a^{HA}K_b^{A} = \frac{[H^+][A^-]}{[HA]} \cdot \frac{[HA][OH^-]}{[A^-]} = [H^+][OH^-] = K_w,$$

or

$$K_b^{A} = \frac{K_w}{K_a^{HA}}.$$

---

* The use of the term *hydrolysis*, which means "cleavage by water," to describe the basic properties of these salts is unfortunate but nevertheless firmly entrenched. We have, however, tried to make clear that cyanide and acetate ions are weak bases exactly like ammonia, except for their charge.

Similarly, the hydrolysis of the salt of a weak base and a strong acid is the same as the ionization of a weak acid:

$$BH^+ + H_2O \rightleftharpoons B + H_3O^+.$$

In a manner similar to the above, we can show that

$$K_a^{BH^+} = \frac{K_w}{K_b^B}.$$

In general, for an acid and its conjugate base,

$$K_a K_b = K_w.$$

The logarithmic concentration diagram for ammonia (Fig. 4–5) can also be considered to be the diagram for the weak acid NH_4^+, whose acid ionization constant is given by

$$
\begin{aligned}
pK_a &= pK_w - pK_b \\
&= 14.00 - 4.75 \\
&= 9.25.
\end{aligned}
$$

Thus the system point can always be placed at the pH equal to pK_a for the acid form of whatever acid-base system is being studied.

In all the problems we have dealt with so far, the proton condition has been given by the charge balance. In problems where the acid or base under consideration is an ion, the charge balance has additional terms resulting from the inert ion of the salt. For example, in a solution of the salt NaA, the charge balance is

$$[Na^+] + [H^+] = [A^-] + [OH^-].$$

In solutions of normal concentrations, the term $[Na^+]$ and the term $[A^-]$ are both approximately equal, and are very much larger than either $[H^+]$ or $[OH^-]$, which are the concentrations of interest.

To look at the differences between these smaller terms, we combine the charge balance with the mass balances. If the mass balance

$$[Na^+] = [A^-] + [HA] = C$$

is subtracted from the charge balance so that the large terms are eliminated, the result is the proton condition

$$[H^+] + [HA] = [OH^-],$$

which relates the small concentrations of interest.

Example 8. Calculate the concentrations of all species in 0.010 molar sodium cyanide solution; K_a for HCN is 4.8×10^{-10}. There are five concentrations to be considered, and five relations among them:

Equilibrium:
$$[H^+][CN^-] = 4.8 \times 10^{-10}[HCN], \tag{1}$$

$$[H^+][OH^-] = 1.00 \times 10^{-14}; \tag{2}$$

Charge balance:
$$[H^+] + [Na^+] = [OH^-] + [CN^-]; \tag{3}$$

Mass balances:
$$[CN^-] + [HCN] = 0.010, \tag{4}$$

$$[Na^+] = 0.010. \tag{5}$$

The proton condition is no longer given by the charge balance, but must be derived from it by using the mass balances. Adding (3) to (4), and subtracting (5), we have

$$[H^+] + [HCN] = [OH^-], \tag{6}$$

which is the proton condition. Note that we could also obtain the proton condition by consideration of a mass balance on $[OH^-]$. We have two sources of hydroxyl ion, the reaction of CN^- with water,

$$CN^- + H_2O = HCN + OH^-,$$

and the ionization of water:

$$H_2O = H^+ + OH^-.$$

For every hydroxyl ion formed from cyanide ion, a molecule of HCN is formed also. For every hydroxyl ion formed from water, a hydrogen ion is also formed. Thus we obtain Eq. (6), which is analogous to Eq. (3) of Example 6.

If we assume that the solution is basic, we can neglect $[H^+]$ in (6) compared to $[HCN]$, and get the approximate relation

$$[HCN] = [OH^-]. \tag{6a}$$

A further assumption which simplifies matters is that $[HCN]$ is small compared to $[CN^-]$ in (4), giving

$$[CN^-] = 0.010. \tag{4a}$$

These relations are most easily used in the basic ionization constant expression for CN^-, which is obtained by dividing (2) by (1):

$$K_b^{CN^-} = \frac{[OH^-][HCN]}{[CN^-]} = \frac{1.00 \times 10^{-14}}{4.8 \times 10^{-10}} = 2.08 \times 10^{-5}. \tag{7}$$

Substitute (4a) and (6a) in (7) to get

$$[OH^-]^2 = (2.08 \times 10^{-5})(1.0 \times 10^{-2})$$

$$[OH^-] = 4.56 \times 10^{-4}.$$

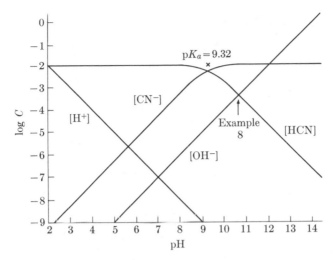

Fig. 4–6. Logarithmic concentration diagram for 1.0×10^{-2} molar HCN or NaCN.

From (2),	$[H^+] = 2.2 \times 10^{-11}$.
From (6),	$[HCN] = 4.56 \times 10^{-4}$.
From (4),	$[CN^-] = 1.0 \times 10^{-2}$.

By substituting back, we see that the original exact equations are satisfied to within 5%.

Comparing this with Example 6, the ionization of NH_3, the parallel becomes apparent. Equation (7) is the expression for K_b of CN^-, and Eq. (6) is the proton condition for this problem, just as the charge balance was the proton condition for Example 6.

In the graphical solution of this problem, the logarithmic concentration diagram for 0.010 molar HCN can be used (Fig. 4–6). Equations (1), (2), and (4) are the same for HCN or NaCN solutions, and are embodied in the diagram. The condition for the intersection is the proton condition, Eq. (6),

$$[OH^-] = [HCN] + [H^+]. \tag{6}$$

Following the $[OH^-]$ line down, it meets the $[HCN]$ line while $[H^+]$ is still small compared to $[HCN]$. Therefore the intersection, $[OH^-] = [HCN]$, gives the answers:

$$pH = 10.66, \qquad [H^+] = 2.2 \times 10^{-11},$$
$$\log [HCN] = -3.34, \qquad [HCN] = 4.6 \times 10^{-4},$$
$$\log [OH^-] = -3.34, \qquad [OH^-] = 4.6 \times 10^{-4},$$
$$\log [CN^-] = -2.00, \qquad [CN^-] = 1.0 \times 10^{-2},$$

which are the same as were obtained numerically.

4-4 BUFFER SOLUTIONS

In many branches of chemistry, particularly in biochemical investigations, we wish to keep the pH of a solution relatively constant over the course of some reaction which produces or consumes hydrogen ions. To accomplish this, the reaction is carried out in a *buffer solution*, a fairly concentrated solution of a weak acid and its conjugate base, which do not themselves enter into the reaction. If hydrogen ions are produced, they react with the base to increase the amount of conjugate acid; if hydrogen ions are consumed, the weak acid dissociates to give more hydrogen ions. The net effect is to resist any change in pH. This effect is illustrated by Examples 9 and 10.

Example 9. Calculate the pH of a buffer which is 0.010 molar in acetic acid and 0.010 molar in sodium acetate. For acetic acid, $K_a = 1.75 \times 10^{-5}$. The equilibria are as usual

$$[H^+][Ac^-] = 1.75 \times 10^{-5}[HAc], \tag{1}$$

$$[H^+][OH^-] = 1.00 \times 10^{-14}. \tag{2}$$

The charge balance is

$$[H^+] + [Na^+] = [OH^-] + [Ac^-], \tag{3}$$

and the mass balances are

$$[HAc] + [Ac^-] = 0.020, \tag{4}$$

$$[Na^+] = 0.010. \tag{5}$$

Substitute (5) in (3) and add (4) to obtain the proton condition:

$$[H^+] + [HAc] = [OH^-] + 0.010. \tag{6}$$

Since the solutions are fairly concentrated, let us neglect $[H^+]$ and $[OH^-]$ compared to $[HAc]$ and $[Ac^-]$, giving merely

$$[Ac^-] = 0.010, \tag{3a}$$

$$[HAc] = 0.010. \tag{6a}$$

Substituting (3a) and (6a) in (1), we obtain

$$[H^+] = 1.75 \times 10^{-5}, \qquad pH = 4.75.$$

Note that this point falls just below the system point in Fig. 4-2, where the concentrations of undissociated acid and anion are equal. From (2),

$$[OH^-] = 5.7 \times 10^{-10}.$$

Checking in the exact equations, we can see that the approximation was good and that the answers are correct to 0.1%.

Example 10. Calculate the pH when 1.0×10^{-3} mole of HCl is added to one liter of the buffer solution of Example 9. The equilibria and mass balances are the same, but the charge balance has an additional term for the chloride ion from HCl:

$$[H^+] + [Na^+] = [OH^-] + [Ac^-] + [Cl^-]. \tag{7}$$

A mass balance on chloride is simply

$$[Cl^-] = 1.0 \times 10^{-3}. \tag{8}$$

Substituting (8) in (7), and assuming $[OH^-]$ and $[H^+]$ are negligible, as before, we obtain

$$[Ac^-] = 0.90 \times 10^{-2}. \tag{7a}$$

That is, the effective concentration of sodium acetate has been decreased by 10% by adding of the acid.

Note that (6) no longer holds since it was derived from (3). The proton condition is now

$$[H^+] + [HAc] = [OH^-] + 1.10 \times 10^{-2}, \tag{9}$$

and assuming that $[H^+]$ and $[OH^-]$ are negligible, we obtain

$$[HAc] = 1.1 \times 10^{-2}. \tag{9a}$$

That is, the effective concentration of acetic acid has been increased by 10%. Adding 10^{-3} mole of strong acid has converted 10% of the salt to the undissociated acid. Substituting (7a) and (9a) in (1) gives

$$[H^+] = 2.14 \times 10^{-5}, \qquad pH = 4.67.$$

The addition of the strong acid has changed the pH by 0.08 unit. Adding the same amount of HCl to a liter of pure water would change its pH from 7.00 to 3.00, a matter of 4.00 units. The buffer does a very good job of resisting changes in pH.

Simple formula for pH of buffer. Let us now consider the general buffer solution consisting of a weak acid and its conjugate base. If we have a weak acid HA and its salt NaA, of concentrations C_{HA} and C_A respectively, there are five unknowns and five equations relating them, as we have seen in the two examples above:

$$[H^+][A^-] = K_a[HA], \tag{1}$$

$$[H^+][OH^-] = K_w, \tag{2}$$

$$[H^+] + [Na^+] = [OH^-] + [A^-], \tag{3}$$

$$[HA] + [A^-] = C_{HA} + C_A, \tag{4}$$

$$[Na^+] = C_A. \tag{5}$$

Substituting (5) in (3) and adding to (4) gives the proton condition:

$$[H^+] + [HA] = C_{HA} + [OH^-]. \tag{6}$$

A very simple formula for the pH of a buffer (Henderson's equation) can be derived if the assumption is made that $[H^+]$ and $[OH^-]$ are small compared to C_{HA} and C_A. Then from (3) and (6), using (5), we have

$$[A^-] = C_A, \tag{3a}$$

$$[HA] = C_{HA}. \tag{6a}$$

These can be substituted in (1) to give

$$[H^+] = K_a \frac{C_{HA}}{C_A}. \tag{10}$$

This equation is useful, but it will not hold if the acid is too strong (then $[H^+]$ would not be negligible), if the acid is too weak (then $[OH^-]$ would not be negligible), or if the analytical concentrations are too small. The solutions used as buffers in practice, however, usually fulfill the conditions for the approximate equation (10). The buffer system is chosen such that the concentrations of conjugate acid and base are approximately equal, giving a pH near pK_a. As we shall see, this ratio also gives the greatest resistance to changes in pH.

The same method can also be applied to a mixture of a weak base B and its salt BHCl. Under the approximation that $[H^+]$ and $[OH^-]$ are negligible compared to the analytical concentrations, the approximate equation,

$$[H^+] = \frac{K_w C_{BH^+}}{K_b C_B},$$

is obtained. Recall from Section 4-3 that $K_a K_b = K_w$.

Measuring ionization constants. Ionization constants of acids and bases are most accurately measured in buffer solutions. The details of pH measurement are beyond the scope of this book, but we shall assume that a "pH meter" is available which measures $[H^+]$ in a given solution.

The quantities $[H^+]$, C_{HA}, and C_A are known, $[OH^-]$ is calculated from the ion product of water (2), and $[HA]$ and $[A^-]$ are calculated from Eqs. (3) and (6):

$$[HA] = C_{HA} + [OH^-] - [H^+], \tag{6}$$

$$[A^-] = C_A - [OH^-] + [H^+]. \tag{3}$$

Then K_a can be calculated from (1):

$$K_a = \frac{[H^+](C_A - [OH^-] + [H^+])}{C_{HA} + [OH^-] - [H^+]}. \tag{11}$$

To obtain the theoretically significant activity constant, activity coefficient corrections must be applied, or else K_a must be extrapolated to zero ionic strength.

Dilute buffer solutions. We mentioned that Eq. (10) breaks down if $[H^+]$ or $[OH^-]$ is not negligible compared to C_{HA} and C_A. Equation (10) implies that the pH of a buffer is independent of its concentration so long as the ratio of acid to conjugate base is held constant. This certainly cannot be true at all concentrations, since when both C_{HA} and C_A are zero, the pH is 7.00. In applying (10) it is important to know how dilute the buffer can be before this simple approximation breaks down.

The exact equation for $[H^+]$ may be obtained by substituting (2) in (11):

$$[H^+](C_A[H^+] - K_w + [H^+]^2) = K_a(C_{HA}[H^+] + K_w - [H^+]^2).$$

This is of third degree in $[H^+]$, but linear in the analytical concentrations. To show the variation of pH with concentration, a given ratio C_{HA}/C_A is assumed, and the equation solved for C_A:

$$C_A = \frac{\left(\dfrac{K_a}{[H^+]} + 1\right)\left([H^+] - \dfrac{K_w}{[H^+]}\right)}{\left(\dfrac{K_a C_{HA}}{[H^+]C_A} - 1\right)}. \tag{14}$$

If values are assumed for $[H^+]$ and C_A is calculated, the form of the function is easily obtained. Note that C_A is a positive number only for values of $[H^+]$ between 10^{-7} (below this the numerator is negative) and the value given by Eq. (10) (above this the denominator is negative).

Figure 4-7 shows the relation of the pH of an equimolar sodium acetate-acetic acid buffer ($K_a = 1.75 \times 10^{-5}$, $C_{HA}/C_A = 1$) to its concentration. The pH is plotted as a function of $-\log C_A$. Note that Eq. (10) holds in this case only when the concentration is greater than about 10^{-3} mole/liter. Below that concentration $[H^+]$ is not negligible; below a concentration of 10^{-6} mole/liter, $[OH^-]$ is not negligible either.

On the other hand, if (10) predicts that the pH of the buffer is 7.00, the equation will apply for all concentrations. The more acidic or basic the high-concentration limit, the higher is the concentration where (10) fails. On the acid side, (10) fails at a concentration about 20 times K_a; on the basic side (10) fails at a concentration about 20 times K_b. It is

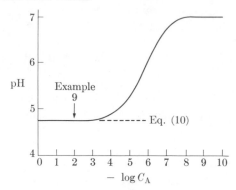

Fig. 4–7.   pH of an equimolar acetic acid-sodium acetate buffer as a function of analytical concentration. Note that the simple formula (10) applies at concentrations above 10^{-3} molar, and that pH = 7.00 at concentrations below 10^{-8} molar.

always wise, in any case, to check the results of your calculation by substitution in the original exact equations (1) through (4) to see whether they hold to the desired accuracy.

The buffer index. We saw in Example 10 that a buffer resists any change in pH resulting from the addition of a strong acid. Adding 10^{-3} mole/liter of strong acid changed the pH by only 0.08 unit. A measure of the buffer capacity is the amount of strong acid or strong base required to change the pH by a given amount. The larger this quantity is, the better the buffer.

It is most convenient mathematically to define the buffer index* to be a derivative,

$$\beta = \frac{dC_b}{dpH}. \tag{15}$$

The addition of dC_b moles of strong base to one liter of the buffer increases the pH and increases the analytical concentration of the basic component (sodium acetate) by an amount dC_b at the expense of the acid component (acetic acid). Since the addition of strong acid produces the reverse effect, we can also write β in terms of the concentration of strong acid C_a added:

$$\beta = -\frac{dC_a}{dpH}.$$

In either case, β is a positive number.

---

* Students who have not had calculus can ignore this derivation, but should study the results obtained, particularly Fig. 4–8. The buffer index was first introduced by Van Slyke in 1922. It is sometimes referred to as the *inverse slope*, this term being derived from its relation to the titration curve, the slope of which is dpH/dC_b.

The buffer index of a monoprotic acid and its conjugate base has a simple form, which can be easily derived by differentiating the charge balance. Consider a solution containing C_b moles NaOH, C_a moles HCl and C moles of a weak acid both as HA and as A^-. The equilibria are

$$[H^+][A^-] = K_a[HA], \tag{1}$$

$$[H^+][OH^-] = K_w. \tag{2}$$

The mass balances are

$$[Na^+] = C_b, \tag{16}$$

$$[Cl^-] = C_a, \tag{17}$$

$$[HA] + [A^-] = C. \tag{18}$$

The charge balance is

$$[H^+] + [Na^+] = [OH^-] + [Cl^-] + [A^-]. \tag{19}$$

Combining (1) and (18) gives

$$[A^-] = \frac{CK_a}{K_a + [H^+]}. \tag{20}$$

Substituting (2), (16), (17), and (20) in (19) yields

$$C_b = C_a + \frac{K_w}{[H^+]} - [H^+] + \frac{CK_a}{K_a + [H^+]}. \tag{21}$$

The buffer index is obtained by differentiating (21), but we must first express β as a derivative with respect to $[H^+]$. Since

$$pH = -\log_{10}[H^+] = -\frac{1}{2.303} \ln [H^+],$$

Eq. (15) can be written

$$\beta = \frac{dC_b}{dpH} = \frac{dC_b}{d[H^+]} \frac{d[H^+]}{dpH} = -2.303[H^+]\frac{dC_b}{d[H^+]}. \tag{22}$$

Differentiating (21) with respect to $[H^+]$ holding C_a constant and using (22), we have the desired expression for the buffer index:

$$\beta = 2.303 \left(\frac{K_w}{[H^+]} + [H^+] + \frac{CK_a[H^+]}{(K_a + [H^+])^2} \right). \tag{23}$$

Thus when we know the pH of the buffer, we calculate its buffer index by direct substitution in (23). The first two terms result from the buffering effect of water, and the third term results from the buffering effect of the conjugate acid-base pair. An identical relation is obtained for the buffer index of a mixture of a weak base B and its conjugate acid BH^+, if K_a is the ionization constant of BH^+.

Example 11. Using the buffer index, calculate the pH when 1.0×10^{-3} mole of HCl are added to one liter of the buffer solution of Example 9. In Example 9, we found that pH = 4.75, or $[H^+] = 1.75 \times 10^{-5}$. The total concentration of acetic acid and acetate ion is $C = 2.0 \times 10^{-2}$. From Eq. (23), we calculate

$$\beta = 2.303(5.7 \times 10^{-10} + 1.75 \times 10^{-5} + 5.0 \times 10^{-3}) = 1.15 \times 10^{-2}.$$

The change in pH is calculated from the definition of the buffer index:

$$\beta = -\frac{dC_a}{d\text{pH}}.$$

If the differentials are approximated by small differences, the change in pH is given by

$$\Delta\text{pH} = -\frac{\Delta C_a}{\beta} = \frac{1.0 \times 10^{-3}}{1.15 \times 10^{-2}} = -0.086.$$

Thus the pH of the buffer after addition of the strong acid is

$$\text{pH} = 4.75 - 0.086 = 4.66,$$

which agrees with the answer to Example 10 within the rounding-off error.

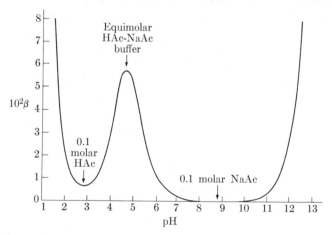

Fig. 4-8. Buffer index of 0.10 molar acetic acid as a function of pH. The minima correspond to pure acetic acid and sodium acetate, the maximum to the equimolar mixture of the two.

Figure 4–8 shows the variation in buffer index with pH for 0.10 molar acetic acid buffers. The maximum buffer index is obtained at

$$pH = pK_a = 4.75,$$

when the concentrations of acetic acid and acetate ion are equal. The minimum buffer index is obtained for acetic acid alone (pH = 2.88) and sodium acetate alone (pH = 8.88).

To obtain solutions more acid than pH = 2.88, it is necessary to add a strong acid, and the large increase in buffer index around pH = 2 reflects the increasing concentration of strong acid necessary to achieve this acidity. To obtain solutions more basic than pH = 8.88, it is necessary to add a strong base, and the increase of buffer index around pH = 12 reflects the increasing concentration of strong base.

Note that a solution containing only acetic acid has an appreciable buffer capacity ($\beta = 8.3 \times 10^{-3}$) but a solution containing only sodium acetate has a much smaller buffer capacity ($\beta = 3.5 \times 10^{-5}$). This means that while a crude measurement of the pH of 0.1 molar acetic acid may give a value close to 2.88, a crude measurement of the pH of 0.1 molar sodium acetate may give a value much more acid than pH = 8.88 unless atmospheric carbon dioxide is rigorously excluded from the solutions.

4–5 POLYPROTIC ACIDS

Up to now we have considered only acids which give a single proton on ionization, and have treated these in detail. A large number of acids can give two or more protons on ionization, and these are referred to as *polyprotic* acids. Because the mathematics of polyprotic acid equilibria is so much more complicated than monoprotic acid equilibria, we shall consider only the very simplest types of problem.

The removal of each proton from the acid constitutes a separate equilibrium, and hence there are always as many equilibrium constants for a polyprotic acid as there are hydrogens which can ionize. The ionization constants for a number of polyprotic acids are given in the appendix. Depending on the structure of the molecule, the ionization constant for removing the second proton may be very much smaller or almost the same value as that for the first proton.

Phosphoric acid H_3PO_4 can dissociate in three steps, and hence has three ionization constants corresponding to the equilibria:

$$H_3PO_4 \rightleftharpoons H_2PO_4^- + H^+, \qquad [H^+][H_2PO_4^-] = K_{a1}[H_3PO_4],$$
$$H_2PO_4^- \rightleftharpoons HPO_4^= + H^+, \qquad [H^+][HPO_4^=] = K_{a2}[H_2PO_4^-],$$
$$HPO_4^= \rightleftharpoons PO_4^{\equiv} + H^+, \qquad [H^+][PO_4^{\equiv}] = K_{a3}[HPO_4^=].$$

The simple structure of phosphoric acid,

$$\begin{array}{c} \text{OH} \\ | \\ \text{HO}-\text{P}{=}\text{O} \\ | \\ \text{OH} \end{array} \qquad \text{(tetrahedral)},$$

is such that removing a proton gives the entire molecule a negative charge. This means that the removal of the second proton becomes much more difficult, and removal of the third proton even more difficult. This is reflected in the values of the ionization constants:

$$\text{p}K_{a1} = 2.23, \qquad \text{p}K_{a2} = 7.21, \qquad \text{p}K_{a3} = 12.32.$$

Each successive constant is about 10^{-5} of the preceding one, a general rule for oxy-acids where all OH groups are attached to the same atom.

The second ionization constant can be even smaller than 10^{-5} of the first if both protons are attached to the same atom. For instance, K_{a1}, for the ionization of H_2O to H^+ and OH^-, is 1.8×10^{-16}, but K_{a2}, for the ionization of OH^- to H^+ and $O^=$, is of the order of 10^{-30}, so that the ratio K_{a2} to K_{a1} is about 10^{-15}. Essentially no free $O^=$ can exist even in the most strongly basic aqueous solutions. In hydrogen selenide, the ratio of K_{a2} to K_{a1} is 10^{-7}. In hydrogen sulfide, the ratio of K_{a2} to K_{a1} is 10^{-6}.

Carbonic acid is unusual in that only a small fraction of the carbon dioxide dissolved in water exists as the diprotic acid H_2CO_3. The hydration equilibrium

$$H_2O + CO_2 \rightleftharpoons H_2CO_3, \qquad \dagger K = \frac{[H_2CO_3]}{[CO_2]} = 2.6 \times 10^{-3},$$

is slow to be established (about 0.1 second) compared to the ionization equilibria

$$H_2CO_3 \rightleftharpoons HCO_3^- + H^+, \qquad \dagger K_{a1} = \frac{[H^+][HCO_3^-]}{[H_2CO_3]} = 1.7 \times 10^{-4},$$

$$HCO_3^- \rightleftharpoons CO_3^= + H^+, \qquad K_{a2} = \frac{[H^+][CO_3^=]}{[HCO_3^-]} = 5.6 \times 10^{-11},$$

which are established in about 10^{-6} second in dilute solutions. Because of this difference in rates, the ionization equilibria can be studied by very rapid flow techniques without appreciably disturbing the hydration equilibrium and the separate equilibrium constants obtained. However, because $[H_2CO_3]$ is such a small fraction of $[CO_2]$, independent of concentration and pH, it is usually neglected in calculations. The first ionization constant of carbonic acid listed in the Appendix is for the overall reaction

$$H_2O + CO_2 \rightleftharpoons H^+ + HCO_3^- \qquad K_{a1} = \frac{[H^+][HCO_3^-]}{[CO_2]} = 4.4 \times 10^{-7}.$$

In more complicated molecules, where the proton-donating groups are widely separated, the successive constants are much closer together in value. In organic molecules with a long hydrocarbon chain between the acid groups, such as succinic and adipic acids, the ratio of the two constants is only 10^{-1}.

Distribution diagrams. Depending on the pH of the solution, a polyprotic acid may exist principally as the molecular acid or any one of its anionic forms. It is a very straightforward matter to calculate the fraction present as each species as a function of $[H^+]$, and a graph of this information provides an overall picture of the equilibrium involved.

Example 12. Calculate the fraction of phosphoric acid present as each species as a function of the pH. The equilibria are:

$$[H^+][H_2PO_4^-] = K_{a1}[H_3PO_4], \tag{1}$$

$$[H^+][HPO_4^=] = K_{a2}[H_2PO_4^-], \tag{2}$$

$$[H^+][PO_4^\equiv] = K_{a3}[HPO_4^=]. \tag{3}$$

The mass balance on phosphate is

$$[H_3PO_4] + [H_2PO_4^-] + [HPO_4^=] + [PO_4^\equiv] = C, \tag{4}$$

where C is the analytical concentration of phosphoric acid. If we assume that $[H^+]$ and C are known, we have four equations in four unknowns.

The fraction of the acid present as each species is the ratio of the concentration of that species to the analytical concentration, for example,

$$\alpha_3 = \frac{[H_3PO_4]}{C}.$$

The index on α gives the number of protons attached to the molecule.

For our purposes, it is more convenient to calculate the reciprocal of this fraction, since this is directly expressible in terms of the mass balance (4):

$$\frac{1}{\alpha_3} = \frac{C}{[H_3PO_4]} = 1 + \frac{[H_2PO_4^-]}{[H_3PO_4]} + \frac{[HPO_4^=]}{[H_3PO_4]} + \frac{[PO_4^\equiv]}{[H_3PO_4]}. \tag{5}$$

Equation (1) gives the second term directly:

$$\frac{[H_2PO_4^-]}{[H_3PO_4]} = \frac{K_{a1}}{[H^+]}. \tag{6}$$

Multiplying (1) by (2) to eliminate $[H_2PO_4^-]$ gives the third term:

$$\frac{[HPO_4^=]}{[H_3PO_4]} = \frac{K_{a1}K_{a2}}{[H^+]^2}. \tag{7}$$

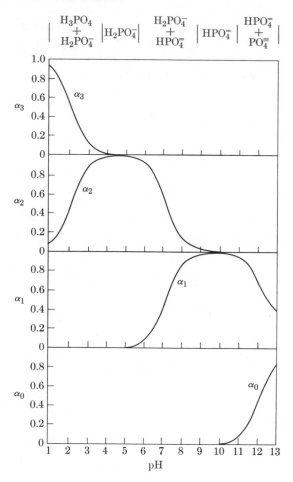

FIG. 4–9. Fraction of phosphate present as different protonated species as a function of pH.

Multiplying (1), (2), and (3) together yields the fourth term:

$$\frac{[PO_4^{\equiv}]}{[H_3PO_4]} = \frac{K_{a1}K_{a2}K_{a3}}{[H^+]^3}. \tag{8}$$

Substituting (6), (7), and (8) in (5) gives

$$\alpha_3 = \frac{[H_3PO_4]}{C} = \left[1 + \frac{K_{a1}}{[H^+]} + \frac{K_{a1}K_{a2}}{[H^+]^2} + \frac{K_{a1}K_{a2}K_{a3}}{[H^+]^3}\right]^{-1}. \tag{9}$$

Combining (9) and (6), we have

$$\alpha_2 = \frac{[H_2PO_4^-]}{C} = \alpha_3 \frac{K_{a1}}{[H^+]}. \tag{10}$$

Combining (9) and (7) yields

$$\alpha_1 = \frac{[\text{HPO}_4^{=}]}{C} = \alpha_3 \frac{K_{a1}K_{a2}}{[\text{H}^+]^2}. \tag{11}$$

Combining (9) and (8) gives

$$\alpha_0 = \frac{[\text{PO}_4^{\equiv}]}{C} = \alpha_3 \frac{K_{a1}K_{a2}K_{a3}}{[\text{H}^+]^3}. \tag{12}$$

Note that the mass balance (4) may also be expressed as

$$\alpha_0 + \alpha_1 + \alpha_2 + \alpha_3 = 1. \tag{13}$$

Figure 4–9 is a plot of the fractions α as functions of pH, calculated by using the ionization constants given in the Appendix. Note that there are ranges of pH where phosphoric acid is almost entirely present as a single species, and ranges where two species are present in comparable concentrations, but no range where more than two species are in appreciable concentrations. This is very convenient for calculations, since at any given pH, all but two species of phosphoric acid will be negligible, and the problem is no more difficult mathematically than a monoprotic acid system. Such simplification is possible only if the ratio of the successive ionization constants is smaller than about 10^{-4}.

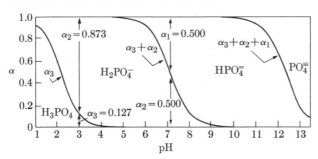

FIG. 4–10.   Distribution diagram for phosphoric acid. A vertical line is divided into segments proportional to the fractions α.

Example 13. Draw a distribution diagram for phosphoric acid. The curves in Fig. 4–9 may be plotted more compactly in a *distribution diagram* such as Fig. 4–10. The curve farthest to the left is α_3, the fraction present as H_3PO_4. The next curve to the right is $\alpha_3 + \alpha_2$, the fraction present as H_3PO_4 and H_2PO_4^-. The third curve is $\alpha_3 + \alpha_2 + \alpha_1$.

A vertical line drawn at any pH is divided into segments by these curves, the segments being proportional to the various fractions α. For example, a vertical line at pH $= 3$ is cut by the first curve into two segments:

$$\alpha_3 = 0.127, \qquad \alpha_2 = 0.873.$$

Segments α_1 and α_0 are very small at this pH and cannot be read from the graph. Similarly, a vertical line at pH $= 7.21$ is divided by the second curve into two equal segments:

$$\alpha_2 = 0.500, \qquad \alpha_1 = 0.500.$$

Segments α_3 and α_0 are very small at this pH and cannot be read from the graph.

Each *region* on the graph is thus labeled with the formula of a particular species; the fraction of a vertical line falling in that region is the fraction of phosphoric acid present as that species. The larger the region assigned to a given species, the more "stable" is that species with respect to dissociation or association with a proton.

pH of polyprotic acid salts. Calculating the pH of a solution containing the salt of a polyprotic acid is not as easy as calculating the distribution diagrams, because of the reactions which the anion of the salt undergoes with water. Depending on the concentration of the salt, the acidity of the solution can vary from the pH of pure water to the pH where the salt anion concentration is a maximum.

The intermediate anions of polyprotic acids are *ampholytes*, and can act as either acids or bases:

$$HA^- \rightleftharpoons A^= + H^+,$$

$$HA^- + H_2O \rightleftharpoons H_2A + OH^-.$$

This means that a solution of pure $NaHCO_3$ or NaH_2PO_4 will have buffer properties. However, polyprotic acid buffers are beyond the scope of this book and will not be discussed.

A distribution diagram such as Fig. 4–10 is helpful in making approximations since the pH of a solution of a polyprotic acid salt of ordinary concentration will be close to the pH where the concentration of the salt anion is a maximum. More helpful still is a logarithmic concentration diagram (Fig. 4–11), the use of which is described in Example 15.

Example 14. Calculate the pH of 0.10 molar NaH_2PO_4. From Fig. 4–10, we see that the salt anion $H_2PO_4^-$ is a maximum around pH $= 5$, and hence the pH of the salt solution will be in this range. The approximations that can thus be made are as follows: $[H_2PO_4^-]$ and $[Na^+]$ are large, near 0.1 mole/liter; $[H_3PO_4]$ and $[HPO_4^=]$ are smaller; $[H^+]$ is smaller still; and $[OH^-]$ and $[PO_4^\equiv]$ are completely negligible.

The equilibria are:

$$[H^+][H_2PO_4^-] = 5.9 \times 10^{-3}[H_3PO_4], \tag{1}$$

$$[H^+][HPO_4^=] = 6.15 \times 10^{-8}[H_2PO_4^-], \tag{2}$$

$$[H^+][PO_4^\equiv] = 4.8 \times 10^{-13}[HPO_4^=], \tag{3}$$

$$[H^+][OH^-] = 1.00 \times 10^{-14}. \tag{4}$$

The charge balance is

$$[H^+] + [Na^+] = [OH^-] + [H_2PO_4^-] + 2[HPO_4^=] + 3[PO_4^{\equiv}]. \tag{5}$$

The mass balances are

$$[H_3PO_4] + [H_2PO_4^-] + [HPO_4^=] + [PO_4^{\equiv}] = 0.10, \tag{6}$$

$$[Na^+] = 0.10. \tag{7}$$

These relations are sufficient to provide a unique solution for the seven unknowns, but the proton condition is more convenient to work with than the charge balance. Note that Eqs. (5), (6), and (7) each contain one term approximately equal to 0.10 on each side. In (5), $[H_2PO_4^-]$ and $[Na^+]$ are both approximately 0.10, and the other terms are small. In (6), $[H_2PO_4^-]$ is the dominant term on the left-hand side. Solve (6) for $[H_2PO_4^-]$ and substitute together with (7), in (5), to get rid of these large terms and obtain

$$[H^+] + [H_3PO_4] = [OH^-] + [HPO_4^=] + 2[PO_4^{\equiv}], \tag{8}$$

which is the proton condition.

Equation (8) may also be arrived at directly by considering the stoichiometry of the possible reactions with water, but more significantly by the following reasoning: Consider the materials of which the solution is composed, H_2O and $Na^+H_2PO_4^-$, to be the "zero level of protons" in the solution. All species containing protons in excess must be balanced by all species containing proton deficiencies with respect to the zero level. On the left-hand side of Eq. (8) are listed the species with excess protons: H^+, a protonated H_2O; and H_3PO_4, a protonated $H_2PO_4^-$. Each contains one excess proton above the zero level, and so each is listed once. On the right-hand side of Eq. (8) are listed the proton-deficient species. OH^- is H_2O less a protonP, $HO_4^=$ is $H_2PO_4^-$ less a proton, and $PO_4^{\equiv}$ is $H_2PO_4^-$ less two protons. Each concentration is multiplied by the number of protons needed to make the zero-level species. Thus what we have done in making the proton condition is analogous to what we do when we make a charge balance, but instead of counting *electron* excesses and deficiencies, we have counted *proton* excesses and deficiencies.

Even if this proton-balance reasoning is not used, it is important in working with these problems to aim directly for the proton condition. Otherwise, the interesting terms in the balance equations will be negligible compared to the large concentrations of salt ions.

Under the approximations outlined at the beginning of this example, the solution of this problem is quite straightforward. Neglecting $[OH^-]$ and $[PO_4^{\equiv}]$ in (8) gives

$$[H^+] + [H_3PO_4] = [HPO_4^=]. \tag{8a}$$

Neglecting all species except $H_2PO_4^-$ in (6) yields simply

$$[H_2PO_4^-] = 0.10. \tag{6a}$$

Substituting (6a) in (1) gives

$$[\text{H}^+] = 5.9 \times 10^{-2}[\text{H}_3\text{PO}_4]. \qquad (9)$$

Substituting (9) in (8a), we have

$$[\text{HPO}_4^=] = 1.06[\text{H}_3\text{PO}_4]. \qquad (10)$$

Multiplying (1) by (2) and substituting in (10) gives

$$1.06[\text{H}^+]^2 = 3.6 \times 10^{-10},$$

$$[\text{H}^+] = 1.85 \times 10^{-5},$$

$$\text{pH} = 4.73.$$

To check the approximations, calculate the concentrations of the other species, using the above value of $[\text{H}^+]$:

From (6a) $[\text{H}_2\text{PO}_4^-] = 0.10,$

from (9) $[\text{H}_3\text{PO}_4] = 3.1 \times 10^{-4},$

from (8a) $[\text{HPO}_4^=] = 3.3 \times 10^{-4},$

from (3) $[\text{PO}_4^\equiv] = 8.6 \times 10^{-12},$

from (4) $[\text{OH}^-] = 5.4 \times 10^{-10}.$

Note that the concentrations fall in the order predicted from Fig. 4–10, and that all the equations (1) through (8) are satisfied to within 5% by this set of answers.

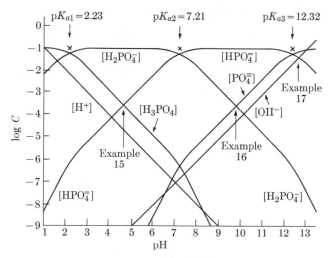

FIG. 4–11. Logarithmic concentration diagram for 0.10 molar phosphoric acid or phosphate solutions.

Example 15. Calculate graphically the pH of 0.1 molar NaH_2PO_4. A logarithmic concentration diagram of the type that we introduced in Section 4–1 can be used for calculations involving polyprotic acids and their salts. Such a diagram for 0.1 molar phosphoric acid (or any of its salts) is plotted in Fig. 4–11. It has much the same appearance as several superimposed monoprotic acid diagrams. Note, however, that at very low concentrations the lines do not remain straight with slope ± 1, but curve downward and eventually attain a slope of ± 2.

The construction of the upper part of the diagram, however, can be done exactly as it would be for a monoprotic acid. The system points are located at the concentration of the acid or salt, and at pH = pK_{a1}, pK_{a2}, and pK_{a3}. From these points, lines of slope ± 1 are drawn downward and joined by short curves, crossing 0.3 logarithmic units (6mm) below the system point, to the horizontal. The $[H^+]$ and $[OH^-]$ lines are of slope -1 and $+1$, crossing at pH = 7, as before.

To find the pH of 0.1 molar NaH_2PO_4, we note that the equilibria (1) through (4) and the mass balance (6) are embodied in the diagram, and are the same for phosphoric acid or any of its salts. The only equation remaining is either (5) or (8). The proton condition (8) is most convenient to use for this problem:

$$[H^+] + [H_3PO_4] = [OH^-] + [HPO_4^-] + 2[PO_4^=]. \tag{8}$$

In the region where $[H_2PO_4^-]$ is largest, all the species on the left (proton excesses) have negative slope, whereas all the species on the right (proton deficiencies) have positive slope. The highest crossing point gives the condition where (8) is approximately balanced. This occurs in this example when

$$[H_3PO_4] = [HPO_4^=],$$

$$pH = 4.72.$$

You can convince yourself that this is the only reasonable approximation by equating each term on the left-hand side of Eq. (8) with each term on the right-hand side of (8), and finding the values of all the other concentrations at each of these intersections. The only intersection at which all the other terms in (8) are negligible is the one we have chosen.

So long as both $[H^+]$ and $[OH^-]$ are negligible, the solution will have the same pH regardless of dilution. As we saw in the numerical calculations of Example 4, $[H^+]$ is slightly more than 5% of $[H_3PO_4]$ when the concentration of salt is 0.1 molar. In a more dilute solution, $[H^+]$ would not be negligible. As a solution of NaH_2PO_4 is progressively diluted, its pH gets closer to that of pure water. In this respect it behaves like the simple monoprotic acid buffers discussed in Section 4–4.

Example 16. Calculate the pH of 0.1 molar Na_2HPO_4. This calculation can be done graphically, using Fig. 4–11. Equations (1) through (4) and (6) are embodied in the diagram. The proton condition can be obtained from the charge balance with $[Na^+] = 0.20$, combined with the mass balance, or directly by considering the proton excesses (left-hand side) and deficiencies (right-hand side) with respect to the zero level of H_2O and $HPO_4^=$:

$$[H^+] + 2[H_3PO_4] + [H_2PO_4^-] = [OH^-] + [PO_4^=]. \qquad (11)$$

In the region where $[HPO_4^=]$ is largest, the terms on the left-hand side have a negative slope, and the terms on the right-hand side have a positive slope. The highest crossing occurs where

$$[H_2PO_4^-] = [PO_4^=],$$

$$pH = 9.75.$$

This point is marked on Fig. 4–11. At this pH,

$$\log[PO_4^=] = -3.57, \qquad [PO_4^=] = 2.7 \times 10^{-4},$$

$$\log[OH^-] = -4.25, \qquad [OH^-] = 5.6 \times 10^{-5},$$

and we see that $[OH^-]$ is 20% of $[PO_4^=]$, which is hardly negligible.

The approximate values of the concentrations are now known, however, and it is a straightforward matter to obtain a numerical solution. Neglecting $[H^+]$ and $[H_3PO_4]$ in (11) gives

$$[H_2PO_4^-] = [OH^-] + [PO_4^=]. \qquad (11a)$$

From the mass balance (6), assuming $[HPO_4^=]$ is large compared to the other species, we have

$$[HPO_4^=] = 0.10. \qquad (6b)$$

Dividing (3) by (4) and substituting (6b) gives

$$[PO_4^=] = 4.8[OH^-].$$

Substituting this in (11a) gives

$$[H_2PO_4^-] = 5.8[OH^-]. \qquad (12)$$

Since we know $[HPO_4^=]$ and have a relation between the other concentrations and $[OH^-]$, we want a relation which involves only $[HPO_4^=]$, $[H_2PO_4^-]$, and $[OH^-]$. Dividing (2) by (4) gives

$$[HPO_4^=] = 6.15 \times 10^{+6}[H_2PO_4^-][OH^-]. \qquad (13)$$

Substituting (6b) and (12) in (13) gives

$$[OH^-] = 5.3 \times 10^{-5},$$

$$pH = 9.72,$$

which is very close to the value (9.75) obtained graphically in spite of the poor approximation of neglecting $[OH^-]$ in the graphical calculation. The largest error that would be incurred in the graphical method would result if the $[OH^-]$ and the $[PO_4^{\equiv}]$ curves coincided, and this would make the pH in error by only 0.15 logarithmic units.

EXAMPLE 17. Calculate the pH of 0.10 molar Na_3PO_4. For this salt, the proton condition is

$$[H^+] + 3[H_3PO_4] + 2[H_2PO_4^-] + [HPO_4^=] = [OH^-],$$

and in the region where $[PO_4^{\equiv}]$ is predominant, all terms except $[HPO_4^=]$ on the left-hand side are negligible. The pH of the solution is given by the intersection of the curves,

$$[HPO_4^=] = [OH^-],$$

$$pH = 12.60.$$

This point is marked on Fig. 4–11. At this pH, reading from the graph, we have

$$\log [OH^-] = -1.40, \qquad [OH^-] = 4.0 \times 10^{-2},$$

$$\log [HPO_4^=] = -1.40, \qquad [HPO_4^=] = 4.0 \times 10^{-2},$$

$$\log [PO_4^{\equiv}] = -1.16, \qquad [PO_4^{\equiv}] = 6.9 \times 10^{-2},$$

$$\log [H_2PO_4^-] = -6.65, \qquad [H_2PO_4^-] = 2.2 \times 10^{-7}.$$

The other concentrations are less than 10^{-9}. The approximations made were good to within the accuracy of the graph. Note that Na_3PO_4 is almost as strong a base as NaOH.

PROBLEMS

In solving the following problems, use the equilibrium constants given in the tables in the appendix. Be sure to check any approximations you make by substituting the answers in the exact equations. Try using logarithmic concentration diagrams for some of the problems.

Find the concentrations of all species and the pH of the following solutions.

1. 5.3×10^{-3} molar acetic acid

2. 0.40 molar acetic acid

3. 0.10 molar HCN

4. 1.0×10^{-6} molar HF

5. Because of the highly polar character of HF, its degree of ionization is rather sensitive to the presence of other ions in solution. For example, the concentration ionization constant of HF at 25°C in 0.5 molar $NaClO_4$ solutions is 1.23×10^{-3}. Calculate the pH of a 1.0×10^{-3} molar HF

solution in 0.5 molar $NaClO_4$, and compare with the results of Example 2 in the text.

6. At 15°C, the ionization constant of HF is 7.9×10^{-4}, and the ion product of water is 4.51×10^{-15}. Calculate the concentrations of all species and the pH of a 2.0×10^{-4} molar solution of HF in water at 15°C.

*7. Sulfuric acid is completely dissociated to H^+ and HSO_4^- in solutions more dilute than 0.1 mole/liter. The HSO_4^- ion further dissociates to H^+ and $SO_4^=$ with an equilibrium constant $K_a = 1.02 \times 10^{-2}$. Calculate the pH of sulfuric acid solutions as a function of concentration over the range from 10^{-1} mole/liter to 10^{-9} mole/liter, and plot as in Fig. 4–1. Note that Eq. (5) of Section 4–1 does *not* apply to this system.

Calculate the pH of the following solutions.

8. 4.0×10^{-2} molar trimethylamine

9. 1.0×10^{-3} molar pyridine

10. 1.0×10^{-3} molar dimethylamine

*11. 1.0×10^{-6} molar ammonia

12. 0.25 molar NaCN

13. 5.0×10^{-2} molar NaF

14. 1.0×10^{-3} molar sodium acetate

15. 4.0×10^{-6} molar NH_4Cl

16. 1.0×10^{-1} molar $NaHSO_4$

17. 1.0×10^{-1} molar Na_2SO_4

*18. Solve exactly the four simultaneous equations governing the ionization of a weak base, to obtain the equation analogous to Eq. (5) of Section 4–1. Plot this as in Fig. 4–1, for ethylamine, $pK_b = 3.33$.

Calculate the pH of each of the following solutions and its buffer index.

19. 1.0×10^{-2} mole HAc and 2.0×10^{-2} mole NaAc per liter

20. 2.0×10^{-2} mole KCN and 2.0×10^{-2} mole HCN per liter

21. 1.0×10^{-2} mole pyridine and 5.0×10^{-3} mole HCl per liter

*22. 1.0×10^{-5} mole NH_3 and 2.0×10^{-5} mole NH_4Cl per liter

23. The imidazole group is an important constituent of many enzymes which catalyze hydrolytic reactions. Imidazole itself is a weak base:

$$\begin{array}{ccc} HN\text{———}CH & & HN\text{———}CH \\ | \quad\quad \| & +\ H^+\ = & | \quad\quad \| \\ HC \quad\ CH & & HC \quad\ CH \\ \diagdown\ \diagup & & \diagdown\ \diagup \\ N & & N_+ \\ & & | \\ & & H \end{array}$$

with $pK_b = 7.09$. Find the ratio of basic to acidic form which will produce a pH of 7.00. Will this pH be affected by diluting the mixture?

*24. The pH of a solution containing 2.20 gm of KIO_3 and 1.80 gm of HIO_3 in 100 ml was measured potentiometrically to be 1.32. Calculate the concentration ionization constant K_a for HIO_3. Calculate activity coefficients from the Davies equation (Section 2–4) and obtain the activity ionization constant K_a^0.

*25. Show that Eq. (23) of Section 4–4 gives the buffer index of a solution containing a weak base B and its conjugate acid BH^+, if K_a is the ionization constant of BH^+.

*26. Derive an expression giving the buffer index of a solution containing only a strong acid or a strong base. Show that the minimum buffer index occurs at the pH of pure water. What is the buffer index of pure water?

*27. Differentiate Eq. (23) to find the conditions for maximum and minimum buffer index. Under what restrictions, if any, do the following theorems apply? (a) The buffer index is a maximum when the concentrations of conjugate acid and base are equal. (b) The buffer index is a minimum in solutions containing only the acid or its conjugate base.

28. Draw a distribution diagram for hydrogen sulfide.

29. Using the equilibrium constants given in the text, plot the fraction of carbonic acid existing as each of the four forms: CO_2 (aq), H_2CO_3, HCO_3^-, and $CO_3^=$, as functions of pH, as in Fig. 4–9. From this diagram what can you conclude about the importance of $[H_2CO_3]$ in any mass balance relation? Show that the use of K_{a1} and K_{a2}, as listed in the Appendix, introduce less than 1% error in calculations of $[HCO_3^-]$ and $[CO_3^=]$ regardless of the pH.

30. Calculate the pH of 0.10 molar H_3PO_4.

31. Calculate the pH of 0.10 molar NaH_2AsO_4.

32. Calculate the pH of 1.0×10^{-3} molar NaH_2PO_4. Compare with Example 14.

33. Calculate the analytical concentration of Na_2HPO_4 at which $[OH^-] = [PO_4^=]$. Find the pH of this solution graphically and numerically. What error is involved in using the graphical method?

34. Calculate the pH of 0.1 molar $NaHCO_3$ and 0.1 molar Na_2CO_3.

35. Potassium hydrogen phthalate is often used as a standard for pH calibrations. Calculate the pH of an 0.10 molar solution of this salt.

36. Under certain conditions the pH of a solution of NaHA is given by the equation

$$pH = \tfrac{1}{2}(pK_{a1} + pK_{a2}),$$

where K_{a1} and K_{a2} are ionization constants of H_2A. Derive the equation, and note what approximations are necessary.

*37. Calculate the amount of 0.10 molar acetic acid required to dissolve 5.83 mg of $M(gOH)_2$, and the pH of the saturated solution.

*38. Calculate the volume of a buffer containing 0.050 mole NH_3 and 0.050 mole NH_4Cl per liter, required to dissolve 5.83 mg $Mg(OH)_2$.

*39. To 10 ml of a solution, 0.20 molar in $MgCl_2$ and 0.40 molar in NH_4Cl, 5.0 ml of 1.0 molar NH_3 are added. What fraction of the magnesium precipitates as $Mg(OH)_2$?

*40. At what pH is the solubility of silver azide the same as the solubility of silver iodate? What is this solubility?

*41. What error is introduced into the calculation of the solubility of $BaSO_4$ in 0.10 molar HNO_3 by neglecting $[HSO_4^-]$?

EPILOGUE

Now we sat on the highest point of the pinnacle. Patches of sunlight and cloud drifted over the little robin's-egg-blue lakes, the forested slopes, and the valley beyond. Above us, shrouded in mist, was the ice and rock of the main peak, but we ignored it in our satisfaction in reaching the summit of this little fragment of the main ridge.

"Too bad," I said to my friend, "Someone else has been here before us. I found a sardine can under a rock here." As I tossed him the bit of rusty metal, a slip of yellowed paper fell out. He picked it up and read it.

"Do you know who left this here?" He mentioned a name I had heard often in connection with these mountains.

"He led an expedition to the Himalayas last year, didn't he? Perhaps our little climb was not so insignificant after all."

Answers to Problems

CHAPTER 1. MATHEMATICAL BACKGROUND.

1. $S = 4.0 \times 10^{-5}$, $[Pb^{++}] = 4.0 \times 10^{-5}$, $[IO_3^-] = 8.0 \times 10^{-5}$
2. $[Ba^{++}] = 1.0 \times 10^{-2}$, $[SO_4^=] = 1.0 \times 10^{-8}$
3. $[Ag^+] = 1.34 \times 10^{-5}$, $[Cl^-] = 1.33 \times 10^{-5}$
4. $[H^+] = 2.4 \times 10^{-7}$ $[HCN] = 1.00 \times 10^{-4}$
   $[CN^-] = 2.0 \times 10^{-7}$ $[OH^-] = 4.2 \times 10^{-8}$
5. $[OH^-] = 4.56 \times 10^{-4}$ $[HCN] = 4.56 \times 10^{-4}$
   $[H^+] = 2.2 \times 10^{-11}$ $[CN^-] = 1.0 \times 10^{-2}$
6. Combine equations to give a quadratic such as

$$5.20 \times 10^4 [HgOH^+]^2 + [HgOH^+] = 9.76 \times 10^{-3}.$$

Use the quadratic formula on this, and obtain:

$[HgOH^+] = 4.23 \times 10^{-4}$, $[H^+] = 4.40 \times 10^{-3}$,
$[Hg^{++}] = 9.34 \times 10^{-3}$.

7. Neglect linear term. $[Cl^-] - 0.427$
8. Neglect quadratic term to get $[NH_3] = 1.53 \times 10^{-6}$. Use this to evaluate the quadratic term in a second approximation. $[NH_3] = 1.52 \times 10^{-6}$
9. (a) 2.19   (b) 6.89   (c) 8.37   (d) 0.04   (e) −0.67
   (f) 9.11   (g) 1.64   (h) 13.19   (i) 14.04   (j) 4.36
10. (a) 3.7×10^{-11} (b) 3.55×10^{-33}
    (c) 5.0×10^{-42} (d) 2.9×10^{-7}
11. $pH + pOH = 14.00$
12. $pH = pK_a - \log R$ $pOH = 14.00 - pK_a + \log R$

CHAPTER 2. SOLUBILITY.

1. 1.33×10^{-5} mole/liter   2. 1.18×10^{-3} mole/liter
3. 1.58×10^{-2} mole/liter   4. 6.9×10^{-4} mole/liter
5. 1.96×10^{-4} 6. 2.46×10^{-9} 7. 3.18×10^{-10}
8. (a) 0.404 gm/liter   (b) 3.26×10^{-4} gm/liter
9. $pH = 10.52$ 10. 27.2 mg   11. No precipitation
12. 14.3 mg   13. 26.6 mg
14. 3.16×10^{-7} mole/liter   15. 1.56×10^{-5} mole/liter
16. 1.26×10^{-4} mole/liter   17. 6.6×10^{-7} mole/liter

18. Solve the cubic equation

$$S^3 + 1.0 \times 10^{-4} S^2 - 1.65 \times 10^{-10} = 0$$

by plotting it and finding the intersection with the S-axis.
$S = 1.15 \times 10^{-3}$ mole/liter

19. (a) 97.5%   (b) 99.5%

20. (a) 0.085%
    (b) 0.021% calculated from solubility product alone; actually nearer to the answer of part (a) when complex formation is included
    (c) 0.063% calculated from solubility product alone; actually slightly greater

21. 0.229 gm   22. 14.3 mg   23. 0.132 gm   24. 9.9 or 18.7 ml (Sufficient dilution causes the precipitate to partially redissolve)

25. Solve the cubic equation

$$[OH^-]^3 + 3.16 \times 10^{-4}[OH^-]^2 - 3.64 \times 10^{-11} = 0$$

to obtain $[OH^-] = 2.53 \times 10^{-4}$, and thence pH $= 10.40$, $S = 2.84 \times 10^{-4}$.

26. From the mass balances in pure water, we have $K_{s0} = S_0^{z+y} z^z y^y$. From the mass balances in the $Na_z X$ solution, we have

$$(zS)^z(yS + C)^y = K_{s0}$$

or

$$S_0^{z+y} z^z y^y = S^{z+y} z^z y^y + \text{other positive terms in } C.$$

Hence for any positive real value of C, $S_0 \geq S$.

27. The five values obtained for $10^3 K_{s0}$ are: 4.46, 4.47, 4.79, 5.14, and 6.44. The increase is primarily due to the changing ionic strength. (See problem 32)

28. Silver bromide precipitates first. When silver chloride starts to precipitate, $[Br^-] = 3.0 \times 10^{-5}$ molar. The maximum purity which chloride can attain is 99.7%.

29. All the $PbSO_4$ is converted to $Pb(IO_3)_2$.

30. 84.0% of the strontium is precipitated, and more than 99.99% of the barium is precipitated.

31. $\gamma_\pm = 0.818$, $S = 1.63 \times 10^{-5}$

32. If the Davies equation is used to calculate activity coefficients, the five values obtained for $10^3 K_{s0}$ are 2.85, 2.82, 2.87, 2.82, and 3.34. The final value may be high for two reasons. The ionic strength is sufficiently high (0.23 molar) that the Davies equation is no longer accurate; and complexes of the type AgAc (aq) and $Ag(Ac)_2^-$ are formed, increasing the solubility and hence the apparent solubility product.

33. $K_{s0}^0 = 5.7 \times 10^{-5}$ $\gamma_\pm = 0.745$
    If activity coefficients are used, $S = 1.03 \times 10^{-3}$. If activity coefficients are neglected, $S = 5.7 \times 10^{-4}$. Complexes would increase the solubility over these values, but they are very weak. If complexes are included as well as activity coefficients, one obtains $S = 1.04 \times 10^{-3}$. Note that for this

data, a plot of $\log \gamma_\pm$ as a function of $\sqrt{I}$ gives a slope of about 0.4 instead of the value 0.5 predicted by the Debye-Hückel theory. This is because the ionic strength is too high for the limiting law to apply accurately.

CHAPTER 3. STRONG ACIDS AND BASES.

1. pH = 7.47, pH = 6.51

2. pH = 3.10, pOH = 10.90

3. pH = 12.48, pOH = 1.52

4. pH = 10.95, pOH = 3.05

5. pH = 8.41, pOH = 5.59

6. pH = 7.09, pOH = 6.91

7. pH = 7.50, pOH = 6.50

8. pH = 2.18, pOH = 11.82

9. pH = 6.96, pOH = 7.04

10. $[EtOH_2^!] = 2.83 \times 10^{-10}$, $[EtO^-] = 2.83 \times 10^{-10}$
    $[EtOH_2^+] > [EtO^-]$: acid $[EtO^-] > [EtOH_2^+]$: basic

11. $[EtOH_2^+] = 8 \times 10^{-18}$, $[EtO^-] = 0.010$

12. General relation:

$$C = \frac{K_w}{[H^+]} - [H^+]$$

Plots are the same as Figs. 3–1 and 3–2, with $[H^+]$ replaced by $K_w/[H^+]$.

13. If only the salt of a strong acid and a strong base is present,

$$[H^+] = [OH^-].$$

If the activity coefficients are equal,

$$pH = -\tfrac{1}{2} \log K_w^0 - \tfrac{1}{2} \log N_{H_2O}.$$

In pure water,

$$pH = -\tfrac{1}{2} \log K_w^0.$$

In a solution containing 1 mole of salt and 1000 gm (55.6 moles) of water, the mole fraction of water is 0.983. The error in pH is

$$-\tfrac{1}{2} \log 0.983 = 0.004.$$

14. Using activity coefficients gives pH = 0.422. Neglecting activity coefficients gives pH = 0.301.

CHAPTER 4. WEAK ACIDS AND BASES

1. $[HAc] = 5.0 \times 10^{-3}$ $[Ac^-] = 2.96 \times 10^{-4}$
   $[H^+] = 2.96 \times 10^{-4}$ $[OH^-] = 3.38 \times 10^{-11}$
   pH = 3.53

2. $[HAc] = 0.40$ $[Ac^-] = 2.64 \times 10^{-3}$
   $[H^+] = 2.64 \times 10^{-3}$ $[OH^-] = 3.79 \times 10^{-12}$
   pH = 2.58

3. [HCN] = 0.10   [CN⁻] = 6.9 × 10⁻⁶
   $[HCN] = 0.10$

   $[H^+] = 6.9 \times 10^{-6}$ $[CN^-] = 6.9 \times 10^{-6}$

   $pH = 5.16$ $[OH^-] = 1.45 \times 10^{-9}$

4. $[HF] = 1.48 \times 10^{-9}$ $[F^-] = 1.0 \times 10^{-6}$

   $[H^+] = 1.0 \times 10^{-6}$ $[OH^-] = 1.0 \times 10^{-8}$

   $pH = 6.00$

5. $[HF] = 3.5 \times 10^{-4}$ $[F^-] = 6.5 \times 10^{-4}$

   $[H^+] = 6.5 \times 10^{-4}$ $[OH^-] = 1.54 \times 10^{-11}$

   $pH = 3.19$

6. $[HF] = 3.5 \times 10^{-5}$ $[F^-] = 1.65 \times 10^{-4}$

   $[H^+] = 1.65 \times 10^{-4}$ $[OH^-] = 2.72 \times 10^{-11}$

   $pH = 3.78$

7. The charge balance is

$$[H^+] = [OH^-] + [HSO_4^-] + 2[SO_4^=]$$

and because of this, Eq. (5) is replaced by

$$C = \left([H^+] - \frac{K_w}{[H^+]}\right)\left(\frac{[H^+] + K_a}{[H^+] + 2K_a}\right)$$

from which the graph can be plotted. Because of the large deviations from ideality in concentrated sulfuric acid solutions, the use of the tabulated value of K_a at concentrations greater than 0.1 molar leads to highly erroneous results. The acidity of concentrated sulfuric acid is discussed in detail by C. H. Brubacker, *J. Chem. Ed.* **34,** 325 (1957).

8. $pH = 11.25$ 9. $pH = 8.09$

10. $pH = 10.81$ 11. $pH = 8.00$

12. $pH = 11.36$ 13. $pH = 7.94$

14. $pH = 7.89$ 15. $pH = 8.53$

16. $pH = 1.56$ 17. $pH = 7.52$

18. In Eq. (5) of Section 4–1, replace $[H^+]$ by $[OH^-]$, K_a by K_b. Thus

$$C = \left(1 + \frac{K_w}{K_b[H^+]}\right)\left(\frac{K_w}{[H^+]} - [H^+]\right).$$

19. $pH = 5.06$, $\beta = 1.54 \times 10^{-2}$

20. $pH = 9.32$, $\beta = 2.3 \times 10^{-2}$

21. $pH = 5.17$, $\beta = 5.77 \times 10^{-3}$

22. From mass and charge balances, neglecting $[H^+]$, we get

$$K_b[H^+](C_B[H^+] - K_w) = K_w(C_{BH} + [H^+] + K_w).$$

Solving this quadratic gives $pH = 8.62$. From Eq. (23), $\beta = 2.05 \times 10^{-5}$.

23. $[B]/[BH^+] = 1.23$. The pH is not affected by dilution, but the buffer index is.

24. $C_{\mathrm{HIO}_3} = 0.102$, $C_{\mathrm{IO}_3} = 0.103$. Substituting in Eq. (11) and neglecting $[\mathrm{OH}^-]$ gives $K_a = 0.134$. Because of the high concentrations, the activity coefficient corrections are large, but they tend to cancel out. Using the Davies equation, we find $\gamma_\pm = 0.745$ at an ionic strength of 0.15 molar. Noting that

$$\mathrm{pH} = -\log [\mathrm{H}^+]\gamma_\pm,$$

$$[\mathrm{H}^+][\mathrm{IO}_3^-]\gamma_\pm^2 = K_a^0[\mathrm{HIO}_3],$$

a series of successive approximations gives $K_a^0 = 0.160$.

25. Replace $[\mathrm{H}^+]$ by $[\mathrm{OH}^-]$, K_a by K_b in Eq. (23); note that the same form is obtained if $[\mathrm{H}^+] = K_w/[\mathrm{OH}^-]$ and $K_a = K_w/K_b$.

26. Neglecting the last term of Eq. (23) gives merely

$$\beta = 2.303\left(\frac{K_w}{[\mathrm{H}^+]} + [\mathrm{H}^+]\right).$$

For pure water, $\beta = 4.6 \times 10^{-7}$.

27. A maximum or minimum in the buffer index curve occurs when

$$\frac{d\beta}{d\mathrm{pH}} = -2.303\,[\mathrm{H}^+]\,\frac{d\beta}{d[\mathrm{H}^+]} = 0.$$

Differentiating Eq. (23) gives $[\mathrm{H}^+]$ at the maximum or minimum points:

$$CK_a[\mathrm{H}^+]^2(K_a - [\mathrm{H}^+]) = (K_a + [\mathrm{H}^+])^3(K_w - [\mathrm{H}^+]^2).$$

(a) From Eq. (14) with $C_\mathrm{A} = C_\mathrm{HA} = \tfrac{1}{2}C$, $[\mathrm{H}^+]$ for an equimolar buffer is given by

$$C[\mathrm{H}^+](K_a - [\mathrm{H}^+]) = -2(K_a + [\mathrm{H}^+])(K_w - [\mathrm{H}^+]^2),$$

which becomes the same as the above only if both $[\mathrm{H}^+]$ and $[\mathrm{OH}^-]$ are small compared to C, so that $[\mathrm{H}^+]$ is approximately K_a, and the right hand side is nearly zero.

(b) From Eq. (14), with $C_\mathrm{A} = 0$, $C_\mathrm{HA} = C$, $[\mathrm{H}^+]$ for a pure weak acid is given by

$$C[\mathrm{H}^+]K_a = (K_a + [\mathrm{H}^+])(K_w - [\mathrm{H}^+]^2),$$

which becomes the same as the above only if $[\mathrm{H}^+]$ is large compared to K_a.

(c) From Eq. (14), with $C_\mathrm{A} = C$, $C_\mathrm{HA} = 0$, the pH of the pure salt is given by

$$C[\mathrm{H}^+]^2 = (K_a + [\mathrm{H}^+])(K_w - [\mathrm{H}^+]^2),$$

which becomes the same as the above only if $[\mathrm{H}^+]$ is small compared to K_a.

28. In a manner analogous to the text, we can derive

$$\alpha_2 = \left(1 + \frac{K_{a1}}{[\mathrm{H}^+]} + \frac{K_{a1}K_{a2}}{[\mathrm{H}^+]^2}\right)^{-1}, \qquad \alpha_1 = \alpha_2\frac{K_{a1}}{[\mathrm{H}^+]}, \qquad \alpha_0 = \alpha_2\frac{K_{a1}K_{a2}}{[\mathrm{H}^+]^2}.$$

Use the constants in the Appendix to plot the curves. Note that at

$$pH = 7.00, \qquad \alpha_2 = \alpha_1 = 0.500;$$
$$pH = 12.92, \qquad \alpha_1 = \alpha_0 = 0.500.$$

29. The fractions calculated at three pH values are given below.

Species	Fraction of total		
	pH = 3	7	10
CO_2	0.997	0.192	1.61×10^{-4}
H_2CO_3	2.79×10^{-3}	5.39×10^{-4}	4.51×10^{-7}
HCO_3^-	4.19×10^{-4}	0.808	0.676
$CO_3^=$	2.01×10^{-11}	3.88×10^{-4}	0.322

Since $[H_2CO_3]$ is always 0.3% of $[CO_2]$, it will be negligible in any mass balance. Note $K_{a1} = \dagger K_{a1} \dagger K$, to within 0.3%, regardless of whether $[CO_2]$ represents only free CO_2 or the total of CO_2 and H_2CO_3.

30. $[H^+] = 2.15 \times 10^{-2}$ $[H_2PO_4^-] = 2.15 \times 10^{-2}$
    $[H_3PO_4] = 7.85 \times 10^{-2}$ pH = 1.67

31. $[H^+] = 2.44 \times 10^{-5}$ $[H_2AsO_4^-] = 0.10$
    $[H_3AsO_4] = 4.07 \times 10^{-4}$ $[HAsO_4^=] = 4.31 \times 10^{-4}$
    pH = 4.61

32. $[H^+] = 7.25 \times 10^{-6}$ $[H_2PO_4^-] = 1.0 \times 10^{-3}$
    $[H_3PO_4] = 1.23 \times 10^{-6}$ $[HPO_4^=] = 8.48 \times 10^{-6}$
    pH = 5.14

33. The analytical concentration of Na_2HPO_4 where $[OH^-] = [PO_4^=]$ is 2.08×10^{-2} mole/liter. In the graphical method we make use of the proton condition,

$$[H_2PO_4^-] = [OH^-] + [PO_4^=],$$

by neglecting one of the terms on the right-hand side. If one term is neglected, for this analytical concentration, pH = 9.76. If both terms are kept, pH = 9.61. The difference is 0.15 pH units, or 14% in $[H^+]$. This is the maximum error that can occur by using the graphical method.

34. For 0.1 molar $NaHCO_3$, pH = 8.30
    For 0.1 molar Na_2CO_3, pH = 11.37

35. pH = 4.18. If activity coefficient corrections are applied, pH = 4.00.

36. In a solution of NaHA, the proton condition is

$$[H^+] + [H_2A] = [A^=] + [OH^-].$$

If $[H^+] - [OH^-]$ is negligible compared to $[H_2A]$ or $[A^=]$, we have

$$[H_2A] = [A^=],$$

which leads to

$$[H^+]^2 = K_{a1}K_{a2},$$

and hence to the formula given.

37. Neglect $[H^+]$ and $[HAc]$ in the mass and charge balances, to obtain pH = 9.72 and $S = 5.05 \times 10^{-2}$ mole/liter. The volume required is 1.98 ml.

38. Solve the cubic equation

$$[OH^-]^3 - 1.78 \times 10^{-5}[OH^-]^2 - 7.28 \times 10^{-10}[OH^-] - 1.30 \times 10^{-14} = 0,$$

to obtain $[OH^-] = 4.26 \times 10^{-5}$. From this, $S = 1.00 \times 10^{-2}$, and the volume required is 10.0 ml.

39. 72%

40. pH = 3.75, $S = 1.73 \times 10^{-4}$

41. The error introduced in S by neglecting $[HSO_4^-]$ is 0.001%.

Appendix

For any problem where the answer is of some significance, data should never be taken from a textbook or a handbook unless the original references are listed so that the data can be checked and some estimate made of their accuracy. The tables in the compilations listed below all contain references to the original research papers, and should be used whenever reliable data are desired.

J. BJERRUM, G. SCHWARZENBACH, and L. G. SILLEN, *Stability Constants*, Parts I and II, special Publications Nos. 6 and 7 of the Chemical Society. London: The Chemical Society, 1958.

A. ALBERT and E. P. SERJEANT, *Ionization Constants of Acids and Bases*. New York: Wiley, 1962.

K. B. YATSIMIRSKII and V. P. VASIL'EV, *Instability Constants of Complex Compounds*. Translated from the Russian. New York: Consultants Bureau (1960).

G. CHARLOT, *Selected Constants—Oxidation-Reduction Potentials*. London: Pergamon Press, 1958.

W. M. LATIMER, *Oxidation Potentials*, 2nd ed. Englewood Cliffs, N.J.: Prentice-Hall, 1952.

W. M. CLARK, *Oxidation-Reduction Potentials of Organic Systems*. Baltimore: Williams and Wilkins, 1960.

B. E. CONWAY, *Electrochemical Data*. New York: Elsevier, 1952.

R. PARSONS, *Handbook of Electrochemical Constants*. London: Butterworths, 1959.

F. ROSSINI, et. al. *Selected Values of Chemical Thermodynamic Properties*. U. S. National Bureau of Standards, Circular 500, 1950.

For convenience in working problems, a small collection of equilibrium constants is presented on the following pages. These tables are not to be used for general reference, since they are not exhaustive, critical, nor completely correct. Also included are the periodic table, a table of atomic weights, and a table of common logarithms.

IONIZATION CONSTANTS OF WEAK MONOPROTIC
ACIDS AT 25°C

(Zero Ionic Strength)

Acid	Formula	pK_a
Iodic acid	HIO_3	0.79
Hydrogen sulfate ion	HSO_4^-	1.99
Hydrofluoric acid	HF	3.17
Formic acid	HCO_2H	3.75
Hydrazoic acid	HN_3	4.72
Acetic acid	CH_3COOH	4.75
Hydrocyanic acid	HCN	9.32

IONIZATION CONSTANTS OF WEAK MONOPROTIC
BASES AT 25°C

(Zero Ionic Strength)

Base	Formula	pK_b
Dimethylamine	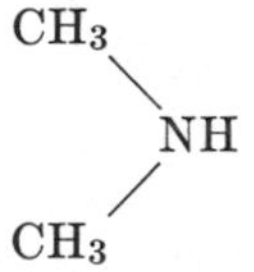 $\begin{array}{c} CH_3 \\ \diagdown \\ NH \\ \diagup \\ CH_3 \end{array}$	2.93
Trimethylamine	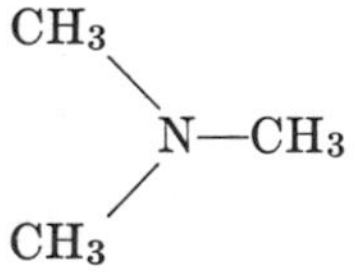 $\begin{array}{c} CH_3 \\ \diagdown \\ N-CH_3 \\ \diagup \\ CH_3 \end{array}$	4.09
Ammonia	NH_3	4.75
Pyridine	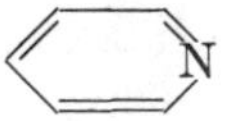	8.82

IONIZATION CONSTANTS OF POLYPROTIC ACIDS AT 25°C.

(Zero Ionic Strength)

Acid	Formula	pK_{a1}	pK_{a2}	pK_{a3}
Carbonic acid	$CO_2 + H_2O$	6.35	10.25	
Hydrogen sulfide	H_2S	7.00	12.92	
Hydrogen selenide	H_2Se	3.89	11.00	
Succinic acid	$HO-C(=O)-CH_2-CH_2-C(=O)-OH$	4.19	5.48	
Adipic acid	$HO-C(=O)-CH_2-CH_2-CH_2-CH_2-C(=O)-OH$	4.42	5.41	
Phthalic acid	benzene ring with $-C(=O)-OH$ and $-C(=O)-OH$	2.95	5.41	
Phosphoric acid (ortho)	H_3PO_4	2.23	7.21	12.32
Arsenic acid (ortho)	H_3AsO_4	2.22	6.98	11.53

Solubility Products at 25°C

(Zero Ionic Strength)

Ions of equal charge		Ions of unequal charge	
Salt	pK_{s0}	Salt	pK_{s0}
AgAc (acetate)	2.40	Ag_2SO_4	4.80
TlCl	3.72	BaF_2	5.76
$AgBrO_3$	4.28	$Pb(CHO_2)_2$ (formate)	6.70
Hg_2SO_4*	6.17	MgF_2	8.18
$SrSO_4$	6.55	SrF_2	8.54
$AgIO_3$	7.52	CaF_2	10.40
$PbSO_4$	7.80	$Mg(OH)_2$	10.74
AgN_3 (azide)	8.54	Ag_2CrO_4	11.95
AgCl	9.75	$Pb(IO_3)_2$	12.59
$BaSO_4$	9.96	Hg_2Cl_2*	17.88
AgBr	12.28	$Ce(IO_3)_3$	9.50
AgI	16.08	$La(IO_3)_3$	11.21

* Hg_2^{++} is a single ion.

PERIODIC TABLE OF THE ELEMENTS

The atomic weights, based on the exact number 12 as the assigned atomic mass of the principal isotope of carbon, are the most recent (1961) values adopted by the International Union of Pure and Applied Chemistry. (For artificially produced elements, the approximate atomic weight of the most stable isotope is given in brackets.)

Period	Series	I	II	III	IV	V	VI	VII	VIII			O
1	1	1 H 1.00797										2 He 4.0026
2	2	3 Li 6.939	4 Be 9.0122	5 B 10.811	6 C 12.01115	7 N 14.0067	8 O 15.9994	9 F 18.9984				10 Ne 20.183
3	3	11 Na 22.9898	12 Mg 24.312	13 Al 26.9815	14 Si 28.086	15 P 30.9738	16 S 32.064	17 Cl 35.453				18 A 39.948
4	4	19 K 39.102	20 Ca 40.08	21 Sc 44.956	22 Ti 47.90	23 V 50.942	24 Cr 51.996	25 Mn 54.9380	26 Fe 55.847	27 Co 58.9332	28 Ni 58.71	
4	5	29 Cu 63.54	30 Zn 65.37	31 Ga 69.72	32 Ge 72.59	33 As 74.9216	34 Se 78.96	35 Br 79.909				36 Kr 83.80
5	6	37 Rb 85.47	38 Sr 87.62	39 Y 88.905	40 Zr 91.22	41 Nb 92.906	42 Mo 95.94	43 Tc [99]	44 Ru 101.07	45 Rh 102.905	46 Pd 106.4	
5	7	47 Ag 107.870	48 Cd 112.40	49 In 114.82	50 Sn 118.69	51 Sb 121.75	52 Te 127.60	53 I 126.9044				54 Xe 131.30
6	8	55 Cs 132.905	56 Ba 137.34	57–71 Lanthanide series*	72 Hf 178.49	73 Ta 180.948	74 W 183.85	75 Re 186.2	76 Os 190.2	77 Ir 192.2	78 Pt 195.09	
6	9	79 Au 196.967	80 Hg 200.59	81 Tl 204.37	82 Pb 207.19	83 Bi 208.980	84 Po [210]	85 At [210]				86 Rn [222]
7	10	87 Fr [223]	88 Ra [226.05]	89–Actinide series**								

*Lanthanide series:

57 La 138.91	58 Ce 140.12	59 Pr 140.907	60 Nd 144.24	61 Pm [147]	62 Sm 150.35	63 Eu 151.96	64 Gd 157.25	65 Tb 158.924	66 Dy 162.50	67 Ho 164.930	68 Er 167.26	69 Tm 168.934	70 Yb 173.04	71 Lu 174.97

**Actinide series:

89 Ac [227]	90 Th 232.038	91 Pa [231]	92 U 238.03	93 Np [237]	94 Pu [242]	95 Am [243]	96 Cm [245]	97 Bk [249]	98 Cf [249]	99 Es [253]	100 Fm [255]	101 Md [256]	102 No	103

TABLE OF INTERNATIONAL ATOMIC WEIGHTS 1961

Based on nuclidic mass of $C^{12} = 12$

(Courtesy International Union of Pure and Applied Chemistry)

Element	Symbol	Atomic No.	Atomic weight	Element	Symbol	Atomic No.	Atomic weight	Element	Symbol	Atomic No.	Atomic weight
Actinium	Ac	89		Gold	Au	79	196.967	Praseodymium	Pr	59	140.907
Aluminum	Al	13	26.9815	Hafnium	Hf	72	178.49	Promethium	Pm	61	
Americium	Am	95		Helium	He	2	4.0026	Protactinium	Pa	91	
Antimony	Sb	51	121.75	Holmium	Ho	67	164.930	Radium	Ra	88	
Argon	Ar	18	39.948	Hydrogen	H	1	*1.00797	Radon	Rn	86	
Arsenic	As	33	74.9216	Indium	In	49	114.82	Rhenium	Re	75	186.2
Astatine	At	85		Iodine	I	53	126.9044	Rhodium	Rh	45	102.905
Barium	Ba	56	137.34	Iridium	Ir	77	192.2	Rubidium	Rb	37	85.47
Berkelium	Bk	97		Iron	Fe	26	†55.847	Ruthenium	Ru	44	101.07
Beryllium	Be	4	9.0122	Krypton	Kr	36	83.80	Samarium	Sm	62	150.35
Bismuth	Bi	83	208.980	Lanthanum	La	57	138.91	Scandium	Sc	21	44.956
Boron	B	5	*10.811	Lead	Pb	82	207.19	Selenium	Se	34	78.96
Bromine	Br	35	†79.909	Lithium	Li	3	6.939	Silicon	Si	14	*28.086
Cadmium	Cd	48	112.40	Lutetium	Lu	71	174.97	Silver	Ag	47	†107.870
Calcium	Ca	20	40.08	Magnesium	Mg	12	24.312	Sodium	Na	11	22.9898

Name	Symbol	No.	At. Wt.	Name	Symbol	No.	At. Wt.	Name	Symbol	No.	At. Wt.
Californium	Cf	98		Manganese	Mn	25	54.9380	Strontium	Sr	38	87.62
Carbon	C	6	*12.01115	Mendelevium	Md	101		Sulfur	S	16	*32.064
Cerium	Ce	58	140.12	Mercury	Hg	80	200.59	Tantalum	Ta	73	180.948
Cesium	Cs	55	132.905	Molybdenum	Mo	42	95.94	Technetium	Tc	43	
Chlorine	Cl	17	†35.453	Neodymium	Nd	60	144.24	Tellurium	Te	52	127.60
Chromium	Cr	24	†51.996	Neon	Ne	10	20.183	Terbium	Tb	65	158.924
Cobalt	Co	27	58.9332	Neptunium	Np	93		Thallium	Tl	81	204.37
Copper	Cu	29	63.54	Nickel	Ni	28	58.71	Thorium	Th	90	232.038
Curium	Cm	96		Niobium	Nb	41	92.906	Thulium	Tm	69	168.934
Dysprosium	Dy	66	162.50	Nitrogen	N	7	14.0067	Tin	Sn	50	118.69
Einsteinium	Es	99		Nobelium	No	102		Titanium	Ti	22	47.90
Erbium	Er	68	167.26	Osmium	Os	76	190.2	Tungsten	W	74	183.85
Europium	Eu	63	151.96	Oxygen	O	8	*15.9994	Uranium	U	92	238.03
Fermium	Fm	100		Palladium	Pd	46	106.4	Vanadium	V	23	50.942
Fluorine	F	9	18.9984	Phosphorus	P	15	30.9738	Xenon	Xe	54	131.30
Francium	Fr	87		Platinum	Pt	78	195.09	Ytterbium	Yb	70	173.04
Gadolinium	Gd	64	157.25	Plutonium	Pu	94		Yttrium	Y	39	88.905
Gallium	Ga	31	69.72	Polonium	Po	84		Zinc	Zn	30	65.37
Germanium	Ge	32	72.59	Potassium	K	19	39.102	Zirconium	Zr	40	91.22

* The atomic weight varies because of natural variations in the isotopic composition of the element. The observed ranges are boron, ±0.003; carbon, ±0.00005; hydrogen, ±0.00001; oxygen, ±0.0001; silicon, ±0.001; sulphur, ±0.003.

† The atomic weight is believed to have an experimental uncertainty of the following magnitude: bromine, ±0.002; chlorine, ±0.001; chromium, ±0.001; iron, ±0.003; silver, ±0.003. For other elements the last digit given is believed to be reliable to ±0.5.

COMMON LOGARITHMS

N	0	1	2	3	4	5	6	7	8	9
0	....	0000	3010	4771	6021	6990	7782	8451	9031	9542
1	0000	0414	0792	1139	1461	1761	2041	2304	2553	2788
2	3010	3222	3424	3617	3802	3979	4150	4314	4472	4624
3	4771	4914	5051	5185	5315	5441	5563	5682	5798	5911
4	6021	6128	6232	6335	6435	6532	6628	6721	6812	6902
5	6990	7076	7160	7243	7324	7404	7482	7559	7634	7709
6	7782	7853	7924	7993	8062	8129	8195	8261	8325	8388
7	8451	8513	8573	8633	8692	8751	8808	8865	8921	8976
8	9031	9085	9138	9191	9243	9294	9345	9395	9445	9494
9	9542	9590	9638	9685	9731	9777	9823	9868	9912	9956
10	0000	0043	0086	0128	0170	0212	0253	0294	0334	0374
11	0414	0453	0492	0531	0569	0607	0645	0682	0719	0755
12	0792	0828	0864	0899	0934	0969	1004	1038	1072	1106
13	1139	1173	1206	1239	1271	1303	1335	1367	1399	1430
14	1461	1492	1523	1553	1584	1614	1644	1673	1703	1732
15	1761	1790	1818	1847	1875	1903	1931	1959	1987	2014
16	2041	2068	2095	2122	2148	2175	2201	2227	2253	2279
17	2304	2330	2355	2380	2405	2430	2455	2480	2504	2529
18	2553	2577	2601	2625	2648	2672	2695	2718	2742	2765
19	2788	2810	2833	2856	2878	2900	2923	2945	2967	2989
20	3010	3032	3054	3075	3096	3118	3139	3160	3181	3201
21	3222	3243	3263	3284	3304	3324	3345	3365	3385	3404
22	3424	3444	3464	3483	3502	3522	3541	3560	3579	3598
23	3617	3636	3655	3674	3692	3711	3729	3747	3766	3784
24	3802	3820	3838	3856	3874	3892	3909	3927	3945	3962
25	3979	3997	4014	4031	4048	4065	4082	4099	4116	4133
26	4150	4166	4183	4200	4216	4232	4249	4265	4281	4298
27	4314	4330	4346	4362	4378	4393	4409	4425	4440	4456
28	4472	4487	4502	4518	4533	4548	4564	4579	4594	4609
29	4624	4639	4654	4669	4683	4698	4713	4728	4742	4757
30	4771	4786	4800	4814	4829	4843	4857	4871	4886	4900
31	4914	4928	4942	4955	4969	4983	4997	5011	5024	5038
32	5051	5065	5079	5092	5105	5119	5132	5145	5159	5172
33	5185	5198	5211	5224	5237	5250	5263	5276	5289	5302
34	5315	5328	5340	5353	5366	5378	5391	5403	5416	5428
35	5441	5453	5465	5478	5490	5502	5514	5527	5539	5551
36	5563	5575	5587	5599	5611	5623	5635	5647	5658	5670
37	5682	5694	5705	5717	5729	5740	5752	5763	5775	5786
38	5798	5809	5821	5832	5843	5855	5866	5877	5888	5899
39	5911	5922	5933	5944	5955	5966	5977	5988	5999	6010
40	6021	6031	6042	6053	6064	6075	6085	6096	6107	6117
41	6128	6138	6149	6160	6170	6180	6191	6201	6212	6222
42	6232	6243	6253	6263	6274	6284	6294	6304	6314	6325
43	6335	6345	6355	6365	6375	6385	6395	6405	6415	6425
44	6435	6444	6454	6464	6474	6484	6493	6503	6513	6522
45	6532	6542	6551	6561	6571	6580	6590	6599	6609	6618
46	6628	6637	6646	6656	6665	6675	6684	6693	6702	6712
47	6721	6730	6739	6749	6758	6767	6776	6785	6794	6803
48	6812	6821	6830	6839	6848	6857	6866	6875	6884	6893
49	6902	6911	6920	6928	6937	6946	6955	6964	6972	6981
50	6990	6998	7007	7016	7024	7033	7042	7050	7059	7067
N	0	1	2	3	4	5	6	7	8	9

COMMON LOGARITHMS

N	0	1	2	3	4	5	6	7	8	9
50	6990	6998	7007	7016	7024	7033	7042	7050	7059	7067
51	7076	7084	7093	7101	7110	7118	7126	7135	7143	7152
52	7160	7168	7177	7185	7193	7202	7210	7218	7226	7235
53	7243	7251	7259	7267	7275	7284	7292	7300	7308	7316
54	7324	7332	7340	7348	7356	7364	7372	7380	7388	7396
55	7404	7412	7419	7427	7435	7443	7451	7459	7466	7474
56	7482	7490	7497	7505	7513	7520	7528	7536	7543	7551
57	7559	7566	7574	7582	7589	7597	7604	7612	7619	7627
58	7634	7642	7649	7657	7664	7672	7679	7686	7694	7701
59	7709	7716	7723	7731	7738	7745	7752	7760	7767	7774
60	7782	7789	7796	7803	7810	7818	7825	7832	7839	7846
61	7853	7860	7868	7875	7882	7889	7896	7903	7910	7917
62	7924	7931	7938	7945	7952	7959	7966	7973	7980	7987
63	7993	8000	8007	8014	8021	8028	8035	8041	8048	8055
64	8062	8069	8075	8082	8089	8096	8102	8109	8116	8122
65	8129	8136	8142	8149	8156	8162	8169	8176	8182	8189
66	8195	8202	8209	8215	8222	8228	8235	8241	8248	8254
67	8261	8267	8274	8280	8287	8293	8299	8306	8312	8319
68	8325	8331	8338	8344	8351	8357	8363	8370	8376	8382
69	8388	8395	8401	8407	8414	8420	8426	8432	8439	8445
70	8451	8457	8463	8470	8476	8482	8488	8494	8500	8506
71	8513	8519	8525	8531	8537	8543	8549	8555	8561	8567
72	8573	8579	8585	8591	8597	8603	8609	8615	8621	8627
73	8633	8639	8645	8651	8657	8663	8669	8675	8681	8686
74	8092	8698	8704	8710	8716	8722	8727	8733	8739	8745
75	8751	8756	8762	8768	8774	8779	8785	8791	8797	8802
76	8808	8814	8820	8825	8831	8837	8842	8848	8854	8859
77	8865	8871	8876	8882	8887	8893	8899	8004	8010	8915
78	8921	8927	8932	8938	8943	8949	8954	8960	8965	8971
79	8976	8982	8987	8993	8998	9004	9009	9015	9020	9025
80	9031	9036	9042	9047	9053	9058	9063	9069	9074	9079
81	9085	9090	9096	9101	9106	9112	9117	9122	9128	9133
82	9138	9143	9149	9154	9159	9165	9170	9175	9180	9186
83	9191	9196	9201	9206	9212	9217	9222	9227	9232	9238
84	9243	9248	9253	9258	9263	9269	9274	9279	9284	9289
85	9294	9299	9304	9309	9315	9320	9325	9330	9335	9340
86	9345	9350	9355	9360	9365	9370	9375	9380	9385	9390
87	9395	9400	9405	9410	9415	9420	9425	9430	9435	9440
88	9445	9450	9455	9460	9465	9469	9474	9479	9484	9489
89	9494	9499	9504	9509	9513	9518	9523	9528	9533	9538
90	9542	9547	9552	9557	9562	9566	9571	9576	9581	9586
91	9590	9595	9600	9605	9609	9614	9619	9624	9628	9633
92	9638	9643	9647	9652	9657	9661	9666	9671	9675	9680
93	9685	8689	9694	9699	9703	9708	9713	9717	9722	9727
94	9731	9736	9741	9745	9750	9754	9759	9763	9768	9773
95	9777	9782	9786	9791	9795	9800	9805	9809	9814	9818
96	9823	9827	9832	9836	9841	9845	9850	9854	9859	9863
97	9868	9872	9877	9881	9886	9890	9894	9899	9903	9908
98	9912	9917	9921	9926	9930	9934	9939	9943	9948	9952
99	9956	9961	9965	9969	9974	9978	9983	9987	9991	9996
100	0000	0004	0009	0013	0017	0022	0026	0030	0035	0039
N	0	1	2	3	4	5	6	7	8	9

Index